Essays on Genetic Evolution and Economics

A thesis presented

by

Terence Charles Burnham

ISBN: 0-9658564-2-9

DISSERTATION.COM

1997

BLANK

HARVARD UNIVERSITY
THE GRADUATE SCHOOL OF ARTS AND SCIENCES

THESIS ACCEPTANCE CERTIFICATE

The undersigned, appointed by the

Division

Department   Business Economics

Committee   Business Economics

have examined a thesis entitled

Essays on Genetic Evolution and

Economics

presented by Terence C. Burnham

candidate for the degree of Doctor of Philosophy and hereby
certify that it is worthy of acceptance.

Signature *Adam Brandenburg*

Typed name   Adam M. Brandenburger

Signature *Vernon L. Smith*

Typed name   Vernon L. Smith

Signature *Edw Owin*

Typed name   Edward O. Wilson

Date   4/23/97

BLANK

Essays on Genetic Evolution and Economics

A thesis presented

by

Terence Charles Burnham

to

The Committee of Business Economics

in partial fulfillment of the requirements
for the degree of
Doctor of Philosophy
in the subject of
Business Economics
Harvard University
Cambridge, Massachusetts

April 1997

ABSTRACT

Ever since Charles Darwin published *The Origin of Species* in 1859, genetic evolutionary theory has increasingly served as the foundation for fields that deal with organisms that arose by natural selection. This thesis argues that economic theory should integrate with Darwinian theory through the creation of a "genetic evolutionary economics". The promise of genetic evolutionary economics is a better understanding of human nature and, consequently, a more accurate and comprehensive economic science.

Economic theory rests on a set of assumptions about human nature. These economic axioms concern human genes, but there is no explicit connection between genetic evolution and economic theory. As a result, human behavior and economic predictions of that behavior diverge in a variety of important settings. Why, for example, do most people save too little for the future when economics assumes that they will save enough? Chapter 2 discusses the difficulties inherent in the standard economic approach. Natural selection theory, the chapter argues, is the best tool for refining the axioms of economics.

Genetic evolutionary economics allows the derivation of parameters that are intractable with standard economic techniques. There is, for instance, an ancient debate within economics about the role of self-interest in human affairs. Chapter 3 builds a genetic evolutionary model relevant to this issue, and concludes that a Darwinian lens removes many of the apparent paradoxes.

Genetic evolutionary economics is a scientific endeavor. As such, it produces specific, testable hypotheses concerning behavior in economically relevant situations. Chapter 4 reports on a theoretical and experimental investigation of gift giving. A genetic evolutionary model organizes the existing data on gift giving and makes novel, testable predictions. Laboratory experiments, performed to test the theory, confirm the evolutionary model's predictions.

TABLE OF CONTENTS

ACKNOWLEDGMENTS

I am grateful ...

To Richard Caves who has been with me for every step of graduate school. He admitted me to the Business Economics Ph.D. program, served on my oral examination committee, and has provided support and advice on every stage of my research. He will always be my role model for an advisor.

To Adam Brandenburger, the chairman of my Ph.D. committee, for finding the best part of my work. His continual faith in me and insightful advice literally changed the course of my research and life.

To Vernon Smith, member of my Ph.D. committee, mentor and co-author, for support and intellectual companionship. His pioneering efforts in introducing scientific methods and Darwinian theory to economics have been inspirational.

To Edward O. Wilson, member of my Ph.D. committee, for writing *Sociobiology* and *On Human Nature*. In these books, I discovered the foundation for genetic evolutionary economics. I would have considered it a rare and great privilege simply to have met the person who wrote these works. The opportunity to have substantive dialogue with him on topics central to my research produced deep, visceral satisfaction.

To Irven DeVore for teaching me behavioral biology and introducing me to the natural sciences faculty at Harvard. Early in my search for help outside of economics, he treated me with respect, served on my oral examination committee, and demonstrated the benevolent, nurturing side of an alpha male.

To Peter Ellison and David Haig for teaching me in their small seminars designed for Ph.D. students in natural sciences. In an academic world that can be territorial, they granted visas to precious intellectual domains.

To my friends Jay Phelan, Tomas Bok, and Joan Greco. Jay Phelan hired me as a Teaching Fellow for introductory behavioral biology, taught me the course material and showed me how to inspire students. His valuable critiques, constant support and humor have been fundamental to all aspects of my life. To Tomas Bok who answered my call for help with a simple: "What can I do to help?" and delivered substantial support. To Joan Greco for detailed review of chapters 1 and 2 of this thesis, and for continually forcing me to relate my work to behavior, not theories about behavior.

To my parents Thomas and Marie Burnham for their love, teaching and support which (along with their genes) quite simply made me what I am today.

Thank you all very much.

Chapter 1: Charles Darwin can help Adam Smith

Human beings arose through a process of evolution by natural selection <u>and</u> this
fact is important to economics. Most economists agree with the first statement. This
thesis argues for the second -- that insights from the field of genetic evolution can
significantly improve economics; specifically, by refining its core set of assumptions about
human nature.

The foundation of economic theory has some well-known difficulties that are not
likely to be solved from within the standard framework. The high stature and broad
influence of economics are based, in large part, upon a rigorous mathematization
following the method advocated by Rene Descartes in *Discourse on Method* (1637) and
Meditations (1642). Neo-classical economics, offering a unified theoretical model derived
from a core set of assumptions about human behavior, has a cohesiveness that is unique
among the social sciences. However, because every result in a Cartesian system rests
upon the starting assumptions, Descartes required them to be absolutely incontrovertible.
Economics has honestly documented the ways in which the economic version of human
nature fails to satisfy Descartes' strict criterion, but has not provided a solution.

Edward O. Wilson argues in *On Human Nature* (1978) that economics can be
improved by Darwinian theory. All social sciences rely upon implicit models of genetic
human nature that, Wilson believes, are circumscribed without an explicit grounding in
biological theory. He states: "Without it [Darwinian theory] the humanities and social
sciences are the limited descriptors of surface phenomena, like astronomy without physics,
biology without chemistry, and mathematics without algebra. With it, human nature can

1

be laid open as an object of fully empirical research, biology can be put to the service of liberal education, and our self-conception can be enormously and truthfully enriched." (p 2)

Natural selection operates on behavior

In order for Wilson's proposed natural and social science integration to be useful, human behavior must be significantly constrained by genes. Evolutionary theory predicts that, subject to physiological and informational constraints, organisms will act to maximize their reproductive success. When the appropriate measure of reproductive success is used, W.D. Hamilton's (1964) *inclusive fitness*, non-human organisms' behavior is consistent with this prediction. In particular, many animals exhibit remarkably sophisticated strategies that appear to be skillfully designed for gene propagation.

Evolutionary theory states that human behavior is subject to natural selection in exactly the same manner as physical traits and non-human behavior. However, the application of behavioral biology to humans presents two challenging but surmountable issues. The first is that until fairly recently humans lived in a different ecological environment. Just as generals are always prepared to fight the previous war, evolution results in design features suited for past environments. The human genome reflects millions of years of foraging, a few thousand years of agriculture, and two hundred years of industrial society.

To the extent that our world has changed more rapidly than our genes, we should expect a degree of mismatch between the two. Useful design features in one setting can be helpful, neutral, or even disastrous in a different environment. Current thinking is fairly sophisticated regarding physical traits. For example, almost no one is puzzled by the fact that the appendix, which arose to help humans survive, now causes problems. However, similar behavioral relationships, such as failures to analyze certain economic situations correctly, are still regarded as paradoxes. The solution to the theoretical difficulties presented by environmental mismatch is a case-by-case analysis of the evolutionary setting, the evolved mechanisms, and their implications in a modern setting.

The second theoretical challenge is the evolved human ability to override certain drives, a talent that appears to be unmatched by other species. This makes the observation and analysis of instinctual human behavior more subtle. It does not imply that modern human behavior is free of genetic history.

There is compelling evidence that human behavior is significantly channeled by our genes. Because of these genetic constraints, human behavioral biology has the potential to resolve several fundamental economic quandaries that are caused by the lack of a precise description of human nature. In the absence of clear data, economic theory can describe the implications of various versions of human nature, but cannot select among them. Biology brings additional discriminatory power by examining the evolutionary consequences of behavior. In addition to this role of refining existing economic axioms, behavioral biology allows the study of human parameters that are currently outside the scope of economics, such as risk attitudes and discount rates.

Now is the time for genetic evolutionary economics

The geneticist Theodosius Dobzhansky said "nothing in biology makes sense except in the light of evolution." (Dobzhansky, 1973) This thesis expresses the view that

3

nothing in human behavior, including economic behavior, makes sense except in the light of evolution. The history of evolutionary thinking can be stylized as an increasing set of domains where Darwinian thinking is considered appropriate.

When *The Origin of Species* (Darwin, 1859) was published, many people were appalled at the thought of a continuity of physical traits between humans and non-humans. In a famous debate, Thomas Henry Huxley ("Darwin's bulldog") was accused, to the humor of the crowd, of claiming a chimpanzee ancestor. Today, everyone who accepts Darwin's view of evolution admits a chimp-like ancestor, and, furthermore, feels no shame at the common origin of human and chimp features, such as opposable thumbs. Similarly, the view that non-human behavior is subject to selective pressure is no longer controversial.

E.O. Wilson's publication of *Sociobiology* (1975) started the modern debate on the genetic roots of human behavior. While this battle is by no means over, the academic literature is filled with articles that assume human behavior is productively studied through an evolutionary lens (see, for example, the journals *Ethology and Sociobiology*, and *Human Nature*). The last several years have seen an explosion of best-selling books on the subject of genetic evolution and human behavior, including Robert Wright's *The Moral Animal: Evolutionary psychology and everyday life* (Wright, 1994), Stephen Pinker's *The Language Instinct* (Pinker, 1994), Oliver Sacks' *An anthropologist on Mars: Seven paradoxical tales* (Sacks, 1995), and Richard Dawkins' *River out of Eden: a Darwinian view of life* (Dawkins, 1995).

Mainstream economic thought has not incorporated a genetic evolutionary perspective. Soon after the publication of *Sociobiology*, economists including Gary

Becker (1976), Paul Samuelson (1983), and Jack Hirshleifer (1977, 1978) wrote

sociobiological papers. The full economics literature is reviewed at length in chapter two,

but the compact summary is that the intellectual descendants of Adam Smith work without

the benefit of Charles Darwin's insight.

Literature cited

Becker, G. 1976. "Altruism, Egoism, and Genetic Fitness: Economics and Sociobiology." *Journal of Economic Literature* XIV(3): 817-826.

Darwin, C. 1859. *On the Origin of Species by Means of Natural Selection, or the Preservation of Favoured Races in the Struggle for Life.* London: John Murray.

Dawkins, R. 1995. *River Out of Eden: A Darwinian View of Life.* New York, NY: Basic Books.

Descartes, R. 1637. *Discourse on Method. [Discours de la methode pour bien conduire sa raison, & chercher la verite dans les sciences. Plus La dioptriqve. Les meteores. Et La geometrie. Qui sont des essais de cete methode.]*: A Leyde, De limprimerie de I. Maire.

Descartes, R. 1642. *Meditations.*: Apud Ludovicum Elzevirium.

Dobzhansky, T. 1973. "Nothing in Biology Makes Sense Except in the Light of Evolution." *The American Biology Teacher* 35: 125-129.

Hamilton, W. D. 1964. "The Genetical Evolution of Social Behavior I and II." *Journal of Theoretical Biology* 7: 1-16, 17-52.

Hirshleifer, J. 1977. "Economics from a Biological Perspective." *Journal of Law and Economics* 20: 1-52.

Hirshleifer, J. 1978. "Natural Economy vs. Political Economy." *Journal of Social and Biological Structures* October: 319-37.

Pinker, S. 1994. *The Language Instinct.* New York, NY: W. Morrow and Co.

Sacks, O. W. 1995. *An Anthropologist on Mars: Seven Paradoxical Tales.* New York: Knopf.

Samuelson, P. A. 1983. "Complete Genetic Models for Altruism, Kin Selection and Like-Gene Selection." *Journal of Social and Biological Structures* 6(1): 3-15.

Wilson, E. O. 1975. *Sociobiology: The New Synthesis.* Cambridge, Mass.: Belknap Press of Harvard University Press.

Wilson, E. O. 1978. *On Human Nature.* Cambridge: Harvard University Press.

Wright, R. 1994. *The Moral Animal: Evolutionary Psychology and Everyday Life.* New York: Pantheon Books.

Chapter 2: Genetic Evolutionary Economics

Introduction

Chapter one makes broad claims about the appropriate role for Darwinian theory in the social sciences. This chapter makes the detailed case for the development of a field labeled "genetic evolutionary economics".

All economists are sociobiologists even though most have never heard of the field. Economics is based on a version of human nature that includes optimization, time discounting, and particular attitudes towards uncertainty. The assertion that these fundamental properties apply to all humans in all settings is a statement about human genes.

What is the appropriate approach to study this genetic human nature? The question is relevant because there is a significant gap between economic theory and human behavior. This chapter argues that genetic evolutionary theory is likely to be a useful tool in refining the genetic version of human nature embedded within economics.

Understanding the world through a Darwinian lens requires careful analysis. The natural selection paradigm has fostered fundamental advances in a wide variety of fields. Progress in those fields, however, required concerted effort by many people over multiple decades. The creation of genetic evolutionary economics is likely to require similar levels of sustained effort. This chapter sketches the road ahead by anticipating the likely difficulties for genetic evolutionary economics and the solution to those problems.

Motivation for genetic evolutionary economics

8

Introduction

The economic model of individual behavior rests upon a set of axioms. While the rest of economic theory is derived, the axioms[1] are assumptions about human nature. It should not be surprising that "small" changes in these foundational assumptions lead to "large" changes in results. Consider that in mathematics changing one axiom about parallel lines creates the field of non-Euclidean geometry. Similarly, altering even slightly the neo-classical assumptions about the origins and pursuit of utility has well-known and dramatic effects on several important results of economics.

This section explores three economic results that depend on specific assumptions about human nature. These areas were selected because there is empirical evidence contradicting the relevant assumptions. Neither the theory nor the evidence presented here is new. They are repeated to make a simple point. The axioms contained within the economic model of individual behavior are extremely important to a wide variety of issues, and there is enough uncertainty about the validity of these axioms to merit further examination.

The neo-classical economic model of individual behavior

A very short description of the neo-classical model of individual behavior is presented here. Every microeconomic textbook contains a more complete description. (See, for example, Mas-Colell et al., 1995, chaps 1-6.) In simplest terms, the model

---

[1] Definition: A self-evident or universally recognized truth, an evident principle or one that is accepted as true without proof as the basis for argument; a postulate. Source: The American Heritage Dictionary

assumes that individuals survey their opportunities and, constrained by various factors including an imperfect knowledge of the world, choose the path that they expect to make them the happiest. This model is discussed below in slightly more detail by examining the human goals, and the method for attaining the goals.

Goals

The assumed human goal is, in a broad sense, consumption. Individuals are assumed to have *preferences* that translate "commodity bundles" consumed over time into a measure of happiness. Beyond certain consistency requirements, the model places very few restrictions on the specifics of an individual's preferences. Humans are allowed to like or dislike anything -- cyanide, torture, hard work, heroin, football games, etc. The model <u>does</u> require that all items affecting happiness be representable as commodities; a variety of non-standard items such as children, infidelity, and self-esteem are "commoditized".

Goal fulfillment

A "rational" person selects the behavior, from the feasible behaviors, that yields the most happiness. Humans, at least rational ones, maximize happiness or, as economists say, utility.

Two additions are required. First, there are multiple, interrelated periods. For example, the decision to work hard today may allow relaxation tomorrow. Individuals are assumed to convert units of happiness between different periods of time using a discount rate. Happiness is assumed to be worth more today than tomorrow -- which, in turn, is worth more than happiness the day after tomorrow.

Second, many important decisions involve uncertainty. Consider, for example, that a person must decide how much of income to save without knowing how long they will live. Uncertainty is dealt with by assuming that people take a weighted average of the possible outcomes.

The result is that people are still assumed to choose a path that yields the most utility. The two additions mentioned above alter the standard prediction only to take risk and time into account. In summary, the standard economic model allows individual goals to vary with few limits, but constrains everyone to maximizing expected, discounted happiness.

Example 1: The invisible hand and the rule of law

> The central problem in the theory of interpersonal comparisons of welfare seems to be an embarrassment of riches -- there are many reasonable ways of making such comparisons and they need not coincide. - Amartya Sen (1982, p 279)

Specific version

How does a person value the lives of other people? One extreme version is that individuals are ruthlessly self-interested and act for their individual gain. Such a completely self-interested person might behave nicely because of societal repercussions, but at the core cares about others only as a means to a selfish end. In economic parlance, a self-interested individual derives utility only from his or her own consumption.

Evidence contradicting the narrow version

The purely self-interested model does not appear consistent with a wide range of behavior (see chapters 3 and 4 of this thesis for more discussion on this point). On the positive side we see a variety of altruistic activities ranging from charitable donations to

11

heroic rescues of strangers. We also have examples of behavior such as vandalism, where the individual is apparently deriving enjoyment from a purely destructive act.

The notion of self-interest may be compatible with the observations above because of the societal repercussions. The altruist may donate to curry favor, and similarly the vandal's stature within his or her group may rise as a result of wanton destruction. So the falsification of a purely self-interested model is more difficult than may be initially imagined.

There are, however, several types of data that pass this more rigorous test. For example, the soldier who jumps onto a live hand-grenade knowing he faces certain death is pursuing self-interest only in a tautological sense. Another source of data comes from the field of experimental economics, where, analogous to biomedical experiments, individuals are put into precisely controlled settings so that their behavior can be studied. One experimental design has an individual (the "dictator") unilaterally deciding how much money to give to an anonymous second party. The result (Forsythe et al., 1994) is that many dictators give substantial percentages to people they never see, and will never interact with again.

More general version

As the Amartya Sen quotation above suggests, economic theory has no difficulty in accommodating an interpersonal component to preferences. The self-interested version is expressed mathematically as U(own consumption) which means that happiness is derived solely from one's own consumption. This expression can be trivially modified to

U(own consumption, others' consumption) which allows an individual to derive satisfaction or discomfort from the lives of other people.

Why it matters

Some of the fundamental results of economics rely upon a narrow version of interpersonal utility. One of the dominant themes of modern economics, and a libertarian philosophy more generally, is that individuals, pursuing their own self-interest, will come to socially optimal outcomes. This is expressed most famously in Adam Smith's line that: "It is not from the benevolence of the butcher, the brewer, or the baker, that we expect our dinner, but from their regard to their own interest.[2]"

More formally this self-interest is one of several assumptions necessary for the "First Fundamental Welfare Theorem" which states that, under certain conditions, a free market will lead to a particular sort of optimal outcome. This "Pareto" optimality is defined as a situation where no person can be made better off without hurting someone else. The formal proof of the welfare theorem is technical, but the basic logic is clear. If there are possibilities for actions that help some people without hurting others, and the individuals know about these actions, then they will take these actions without the help of the government or any other outside party. The result is that there are no actions left undone which make some people happier and do not hurt others. This is exactly the definition of Pareto optimality.

So selfish acts add up to optimal social outcomes -- unless the assumptions are violated. One violation occurs if private acts have effects on other individuals. This fact is well known in economic theory, as shown in the following quote: "But the effect on market equilibrium is significant: In general, when external effects are present, competitive equilibria are not Pareto optimal." (Mas-Colell et al., 1995, ch 11, p 350) So in cases where people are altruistic, envious or spiteful, individuals must be constrained to yield optimal societal outcomes. A less quoted part of Adam Smith's work is the need for self-interest to operate "within a framework of law."

Example 2: Optimal rain forest destruction

Specific version

Economics assumes that an individual's happiness increases as wealth increases. From one perspective, this assumption seems correct. A rich person can always become a poor person by giving away assets. Thus, it would seem obvious that, *ceteris paribus,* happiness will increase with wealth. Furthermore, changes in wealth certainly seem to effect happiness in this manner. Specifically, positive shocks to wealth (winning lotteries, obtaining salary raises, etc.) cause happiness while negative events cause unhappiness.

Why it matters

The concept that wealth is an important determinant of happiness underlies many public policies. John Maynard-Keynes' (1972) essay, "the economic opportunities of our grandchildren," foresaw a world where material luxury enabled societal bliss. Many U.S. social programs target financial goals as proxies for recipients' happiness.

---

[2] *The Wealth of Nations*, vol. 1, bk. 1, ch. 2 (1776).

Environmental policy is importantly affected by a notion of material wealth driving happiness. For discussion's sake, assume that there is a trade-off between per capita GDP and environmental degradation. In other words, more rainforests and less atmospheric carbon dioxide can be attained only by reducing output. Under this assumption there is a wealth-environment trade-off. When this is combined with the assumption that wealth causes happiness, the result is a happiness-environment trade-off. An economist then calculates the optimal rate of rainforest destruction by balancing marginal lost happiness derived from foregone consumption with the costs of environmental degradation. The result is that the environment should be degraded at some rate that is greater than zero.

However, if the assumption that wealth causes happiness is incorrect, then preservation of the environment may decrease output without changing social welfare. There may be a free lunch, not in the quantity of food on the table, but rather in its appreciation.

Evidence contradicting the narrow version

There is evidence that the assumed relationship between wealth and happiness does not exist. Two psychologists, David G. Myers and Ed Diener, have produced a series of relevant articles (Diener et al., 1993; Diener, 1995; Myers and Diener, 1995), including a review of the World Database of Happiness (Veenhoven, 1995), a massive collection of over 500 studies covering more than forty countries.

The authors' conclusion is that only a small part of an individual's subjective well-being (SWB) is caused by any external, objective measure. In other words, income, race, and age have little predictive power for self-reported welfare. Specifically with respect to

15

U.S. income they state: "... a mere +.12 correlation between income and happiness; increases or decreases in income had no long-term influence on SWB." (Myers and Diener, 1995, p 13.) Cross-cultural analysis (Diener, 1995) finds that per capita GDP only weakly correlates with self-reported welfare, and there are important exceptions.

Similarly, there is no trend over time that tracks happiness with wealth. The authors report that 32 percent of U.S. residents polled in 1993 said they were "very happy" -- as opposed to 35 percent in 1957, when in real terms U.S. per-capita income was only roughly half as high. Perhaps the most extreme study (Brickman et al., 1978) reports on lottery winners and people who were paralyzed in car accidents. The individuals had big changes in happiness at the time of the lotteries and accidents, but most people returned to pre-event levels within one year. More generally, Myers and Diener report that "... only life events within the last 3 months influenced SWB." (Myers and Diener, 1995, p 13)

The studies discussed are all based on self-reported measures. To avoid the problems inherent in surveys, some more objective behavioral data would be helpful. One important measure, average lifespan, has increased dramatically along with wealth. Another insight might be found by looking at suicides. While no measure is perfect, suicide rates might reveal something about happiness.

There has been a substantial rise in suicide rates in the United States and Western Europe in the last century (Diekstra and Garnefski, 1995), a period of substantial economic growth. Econometric techniques have been applied to attempt to separate correlation and causation. A study of the U.S. over the period 1940-1982 (Yang, 1992) found no correlation between economic growth and suicide rates, and found that only white male suicide rates significantly correlated with high unemployment. A long-term study of Finland (Stack, 1993) finds a systematic increase in suicides in the 19th and 20th centuries correlated with a number of factors including urbanization and industrialization.

What is the relationship between wealth and happiness?

Economists have argued about the role of wealth in utility functions for some time (Duesenberry, 1949; Sahlins, 1972; Easterlin, 1974), but the mainstream model assumes that more wealth increases happiness. In principle, people could have a utility function of any form, and there is no necessary relationship between wealth and utils. In particular, the evidence seems consistent with a model of humans deriving pleasure from changes in wealth, but no lasting pleasure from absolute levels. There is a paradox here. The individuals involved, not just the economist observers, believe that more money will lead to satisfaction. Goals, financial and otherwise, appear as potential permanent sources of happiness until their attainment. Furthermore, how can a series of upward moves (in wealth and utility) result in no change in happiness? In a physical world, upward steps sum to upward moves. However, the emotional landscape need not follow any such logic, and the evidence is consistent with some sort of ratcheting.

Example 3: Budget deficits and social security

Standard assumption

Economists assume that people make intertemporal allocations (i.e., borrow and save) according to a "discount rate". Individuals look out over the time horizon, understand the trade-offs between consuming today and consuming in future periods, and then choose the amount of savings that makes them happiest. People are usually assumed to have positive discount rates which means that the future is less highly valued than the present.

Two assumptions are crucial here. First, all humans have a discount rate and act according to the mechanism described above. Second, the discount rate is the correct one. People will not, for example, look back and regret having spent all their money on an evening of wine and song or having eaten too much ice cream. They might, of course, dream about having more consumption in both periods, but given the constraints, the alternatives will look the same on Saturday night and Sunday morning.

Implications of standard assumption

Two important implications are derived from the assumption about intertemporal optimization. The first is that there is no need for the government to force people to save. Consider a world without social security or any other type of mandatory savings plan. Now consider a new policy that would force people to save 10% of their income. What is the effect on happiness? The standard economic analysis is that such a policy will unequivocally decrease happiness.

The logic is that the only people affected by the new policy are those currently saving less than 10% of their salary. These people have chosen to save little, because, it is assumed, their expected utility is greater with few savings. This expected utility includes any senior citizen poverty that may result from today's profligacy. A mandatory savings law is bad because it alters behavior, and because people are assumed to choose the

18

optimal behavior. The concept that these people might prefer to save more, but somehow lack the will power, is not accepted within traditional economics.

A second implication of intertemporal optimization reached by some, most notably Robert Barro (1974), is that government budget deficits do not have any real effects on employment and wealth. Consider a government that proposes to cut taxes, but not change spending. What do people do with the tax cut? Barro's idea, termed "Ricardian equivalence," is that people will save every penny of the tax cut. The logic is that individuals realize that their current income has increased, but anticipate the future tax raises needed to repay the increased government debt. Intertemporally optimizing individuals conclude that their wealth is unchanged by the tax cut, and increase their savings by the full amount of the tax cut.

The empirical and theoretical debate is reviewed by Bernheim (1987). Most economists who reject Ricardian equivalence still accept Barro's assumption that humans perform intertemporal maximizations.

A simpler model

Would a person who acted as predicted by the economic model be a saver or a debtor? The answer depends on individual circumstance. People with high discount rates, low current income, or a variety of other attributes might choose to consume more than current income, thus becoming debtors. Similarly, those with different attributes might become creditors.

The empirical evidence that most people have no liquid financial wealth is consistent with the economic assumption of intertemporal optimization. People who spend everything they earn immediately may be using the process economists assume along with extremely high discount rates. Because the parameters used by individuals are unspecified in the economic model, any actual savings pattern is consistent with the theory. However, a simpler view is also consistent with the data. The alternative is that many, even most, people spend everything they have, and are performing no intertemporal optimization of the sort envisaged by economics.

The macroeconomic fields discussed here are extensive, and no short summary can adequately convey all the information. However, the conclusions are robust. If the neo-classical model is wrong because people have no discount rate, or an inappropriate discount rate, there are significant public policy implications.

Conclusion

The existing economic model of individual behavior is simultaneously too loose and too tight. In particular, humans are allowed to like or dislike anything so, for example, there is nothing that constrains an individual's consumption to include enough food to live. This almost complete lack of structure on human goals is coupled with a very precise mechanism for obtaining these goals.

Several areas of economics share a common relationship between the assumptions about human nature and the results of economic theory. The assumptions in general form are consistent with actual behavior, but of limited predictive power. More restricted versions of the assumptions make for precise predictions, but often conflict with observation.

Genes and human nature

This section argues that the universal human nature economists posit is genetic. Furthermore, the study of this genetic human nature should involve the tools of genetic evolutionary theory. The promise of this approach is to find a tractable middle ground between specific/unrealistic and general/unusable versions of economic axioms.

Is there a significant genetic component to economic behavior? In one sense the answer is certainly yes. Without human genes there would be no humans, thus everything that a human does is genetically based. What is actually meant by the question above is: Are there significant genetic restrictions on human behavior?

To answer this question consider what a "no" means. In postmodern language a no would be phrased as "behavior is a social construct." This means that any form of economic behavior is equally likely *a priori*, and any observed human universality in behavior is the product of arbitrary social construction. In this line of reasoning, all humans may pursue some form of self-interest in today's world, but in a hypothetical world they could be taught, *with equal ease*, to act in any other fashion. Thus, the Soviet Union fell, not because it is impossible, or even difficult, to teach people to perform within a communist system, but rather because the teaching was inadequate.

When Adam Smith wrote: "The propensity to truck, barter and exchange one thing for another . . . is common to all men ..."[3] he did not mean that trucking, bartering and exchanging are social constructs. He was exploring parts of human nature common across all cultures, real or imagined. This is a genetic human nature, not in a naive

---

[3] *The Wealth of Nations*, vol. 1, bk. 1, ch. 2 (1776).

deterministic sense, but rather in a subtle, contingent fashion, combining considerable surface variation with an immutable core.

The assumption that a universal human nature is genetic need not imply that genetic evolutionary theory is the right tool for its study. Milton Friedman's classic essay (1953) in defense of maximization notes that expert billiards players act "as if" they understand Newtonian mechanics, but they do not consciously solve the equations of motion. Furthermore, it is highly improbable that studying physics would improve a billiard player's ability.

So there is a logical alternative to applying genetic evolutionary theory to the study of the genetic aspects of human nature. This method is a "billiards player"-like approach, entirely divorced from genes, where behavior is observed, generalizations made, more data collected, results compared to predictions, etc. Economics has followed exactly this course and has had tremendous success.

However, economic theory alone is incapable of choosing which axioms to assume. In principle, a virtuous empirical-theoretical cycle could select the correct axioms. However, in the cases listed in the previous section, and others, the evidence suggests that a narrow version of the axioms is incorrect, but does not provide guidance on the exact form of a more general version.

In summary, traditional economics has run into difficulties in its ability to distinguish between different versions of universal human behavior. A promising and largely untapped source of perspective lies in genetic evolutionary theory, a field with considerable history, technical sophistication, and methodology.

Behavioral biology -- Theory

The simple rule: Behavior maximizes inclusive fitness

The idea that behavior is adaptive predates Darwin, but it was certainly an integral part of *The Origin of Species* (Darwin, 1859), as well as ethology, and is also the basis of modern sociobiology including, in part, the subject more recently referred to as evolutionary psychology. Sociobiology's single most important concept, kin selection, was introduced by W.D. Hamilton (1964) and many of the relevant topics were synthesized in E.O. Wilson's *Sociobiology* (1975). Sociobiology is now standard undergraduate fare as detailed, for example, in Krebs and Davies (1984), and Daly and Wilson (1983).

The central biological premise of ethology and sociobiology is that behavioral genes are subject to natural selection in exactly the same fashion as genes that encode for physical traits. The necessary conditions for evolution by natural selection are straightforward. If genetic variants encode for different behaviors, then natural selection will favor the behavior that replicates more effectively.

Natural selection should therefore select for traits, including behavioral traits, that maximize an organism's reproductive success. For most types of behavior, such as techniques of food gathering or finding a mate, there is direct relationship between the behavior and increased reproductive success for the individual. However, some behaviors seem to contradict Darwin's theory. For example, if organisms are selected to maximize their own reproductive success, why should any individual ever provide help to another individual other than its own offspring? Yet there are many cases where animals act in a way that does not maximize reproductive success.

The solution was provided when W.D. Hamilton (1964) appropriately viewed the evolution of social behavior from the perspective of the gene. Hamilton's contribution was to recognize that the competitors in natural selection are genes, not organisms. He coined the term "inclusive fitness" to properly account for genetic relationships and payoffs. Hamilton states that: "Species following the model should tend to evolve behaviour such that each organism appears to be attempting to maximize its inclusive fitness." As with Friedman's billiards player, Hamilton proposes an "as if" maximization. Natural selection provides a theoretical foundation for Hamilton's maximization that is, however, absent in the case of utility maximization.

A classic example of inclusive fitness theory is a gene that causes an individual to be willing to sacrifice his or her life to save three siblings. When the individual dies performing this behavior it removes one copy of the altruistic gene from the population. However, the laws of genetics imply that each sibling is expected carry the altruistic gene half of the time. The expected benefit to the altruistic gene is three "half" individuals with a total expected value of one and a half. This benefit exceeds the cost and, if such a gene arose, it would be expected to increase in frequency. Thus, by dying for three siblings the altruistic individual is simply acting on behalf of his or her selfish genes.

Inclusive fitness theory says we can expect evolution by natural selection to produce behavior that maximizes the reproductive success of individual genes. In its simplest form inclusive fitness theory seems to say that predicting behavior should be straightforward. Simply write down reproductive payoffs and solve for the behavior that maximizes inclusive fitness.

Three exceptions: Why behavior fails to maximize inclusive fitness

There are three fundamental reasons why behavior may fail to maximize fitness.

Mutation proposes, natural selection disposes

Among competing genes, natural selection will favor those with above average fitness. However, natural selection can only work upon existing genes, and the process is dependent on the process of mutation for its raw material.

As illustration, consider the process of photosynthesis where plants convert light into the energy of chemical bonds in carbohydrates. The efficiency of photosynthesis is defined as the percentage of the energy striking a plant that is converted into stored energy. The optimal "strategy" for a plant is to have completely efficient photosynthesis, and, *ceteris paribus*, any gene for more efficient photosynthesis would be favored over less efficient competitors. If all possible photosynthesis genes were available we would expect the 100% efficient gene to arise through natural selection. However, the highest measured rates for energy conversion are approximately 2% (Ricklefs, 1990, p 194). So evolution by natural selection does not guarantee optimality, at least in an abstract economic sense, even when it has the chance to work for hundreds of millions of years.

Evolution is myopic

Natural selection will converge on local optima and can, theoretically, remain at sub-optimal levels indefinitely.

25

Selection in a changing world, the red queen hypothesis

"Now here, you see, it takes all the running you can do, to keep in the same place. If you want to get somewhere else, you must run at least twice as fast as that!" The Red Queen in Through the Looking-Glass by Lewis Carroll (1872).

Van Valen's (1973) "Red Queen hypothesis" suggests that the adaptive landscape may fluctuate so quickly that evolutionary systems never reach equilibrium. It is possible for the fitness payoffs to change faster than the rate of natural selection.

Conclusion: Application of natural selection theory is an art

There is no algorithm for building evolutionary models. In stable situations, gene frequency will converge to the best of available alternatives. The particulars of stability, availability and local optimality will determine the actual outcome.

Behavioral biology -- Lessons from other species

Introduction

Literally thousands of studies have confirmed the power of inclusive fitness theory. (See E.O. Wilson's *Sociobiology*, 1975 for a comprehensive summary of the early research.) Behaviors that were previously considered anomalies are seen to be consistent with Hamilton's new theory. Furthermore, inclusive fitness theory makes specific, testable implications for animal behavior in many cases. Krebs and Davies (1984) provides a summary of the literature in the area of "optimality modeling". While inclusive fitness theory has its critics (see, in particular, Gould and Lewontin, 1979), Hamilton revolutionized behavioral biology because he provided an integrated, logically consistent framework for the field.

26

This section contains three examples of non-human data, each chosen to illustrate one point. The first example, dungfly mating strategy, shows that small-brained species can execute complex strategies. Hamilton's key insight is that species will act "as if" they are maximizing inclusive fitness. In numerous studies, animals with very limited mental capacity exhibit very sophisticated behavior.

The second example, rats and drinking behavior, illustrate the manner in which genes can channel the learning process. The drinking behavior of rats can be modified by reinforcement of environmental cues, but some cues are more easily learned than others. The cues that are more easily learned are those that were judged to be evolutionarily relevant.

The third example, moths and navigation, concludes that adaptations can have disastrous results in novel environments. Organisms develop behavioral rules with respect to proximate variables that they can observe, not the distal goal of reproductive success. The genes that survive depend upon the relationship between proximate cues and distal payoffs. When the relationship changes between these two types of payoffs, it is possible for previously adaptive behavior to become destructive.

Dungfly mating strategy: Small brains and complex behavior.

Consider the behavior of dungflies, *Scatophaga sterocoraria*, where females lay their eggs in fresh cowpats. Males wait for females, and whenever a female arrives the first male to encounter her successfully fertilizes her offspring. As cowpats age, a crust forms and they become less attractive to females.

The behavioral problem faced by the male dungflies is to decide how long to wait on a fresh cowpat, often with a competing male present. Leave too early and lose potential mating opportunities, stay too long and miss opportunities on the neighboring cowpat. Analysis of this situation requires the tools of evolutionary game theory, which classifies the male dungfly situation as a "war of attrition". In evolutionary game theory the optimal (in one sense) behavior is to act according to what Maynard Smith (Maynard Smith and Price, 1973; Maynard Smith, 1982) terms an evolutionarily stable strategy, or ESS.

Fudenberg and Tirole (1993) show that, under certain conditions, the unique ESS in a war of attrition is a mixed strategy where the time to departure is an exponential distribution. Parker (1970) measured the lengths of time that males spent waiting for females on cowpats and concludes that the stay times fit an exponential distribution. In other words, male dungfly behavior is consistent with inclusive fitness theory.

Consider the sophistication of the dungfly strategy. Humans did not have the tools to calculate the optimal strategy until the development of game theory in the last several decades. Furthermore, most humans, even with a game theory textbook, could not solve for the optimal strategy in a war of attrition. Yet somehow the tiny-brained dungfly has solved this complex problem.

Rats and drinking: Learning is genetically channeled

A study of rat drinking (Garcia and Koelling, 1966) demonstrates clear evidence of genetically constrained learning. The experiment involved training rats to avoid certain fluids. The animals were given two liquid sources, and were taught to avoid one of them through negative reinforcement. Four experimental treatments were performed by varying the characteristics of the liquids and of the negative reinforcement. The two liquids available to an animal differed either in taste or in the audio-visual environment. The negative reinforcement was performed either by electric shock or by radiation.

The evolutionary aspect is revealed in the markedly different performance of the four groups. Irradiated rats use taste to avoid liquids, but not audio-visual cues. Conversely, electrically shocked rats use audio-visual cues to avoid liquids, but not taste. The evolutionary logic is relatively clear. Eating toxic foods produces nausea similar to the effect of radiation. Thus, an irradiated rat "assumes" that it consumed something harmful. There was no evolutionary setting in which harmful foods were correlated with audio-visual cues so rats have no learning ability in this context. The evolutionary relationships with respect to physical injury, simulated by electric shock, are reversed, and so are the learning capabilities.

Moths and navigation: Adaptation and environmental change

Several moth species have developed a sophisticated navigational mechanism that allows them to maintain a constant angle between a light source and the direction of travel. Sunlight and moonlight hit the earth in nearly parallel rays because of the astronomical distances involved. Maintaining a constant angle between sunlight and the direction of travel results in a highly effective navigation system for flying in straight lines. Light rays from nearby candles or artificial light sources are not parallel, and the constant-angle procedure in this situation results in an inward spiral and self-immolation.

Human behavioral biology

Introduction

Inquire "why do humans have opposable thumbs?" and most people will immediately connect the hand's structure to the survival value of delicate manipulation and strong grip. Ask a similar behavioral question such as "why do people get angry when they suspect spousal infidelity?" and most people will not think of an evolutionary answer. However, getting angry at the wrong time can be just as dangerous as falling out of a tree.

This section argues that while humans are a unique species, the tools of behavioral biology can improve the study of human behavior. Human language acquisition is presented as a paradigm for human behavior. Humans show great flexibility in learning culturally dependent language. The genetic constraints on this learning are, however, absolute and empirically clear.

Next, this section discusses the field of evolutionary psychology and the concept of an environment of evolutionary adaptiveness, or EEA. One barrier to thinking about the evolutionary origins of human behavior is the observation that many people are clearly not maximizing reproductive success. Voluntary sterilization and suicide are just two of the acts that seem to destroy any notion of applying the lessons of inclusive fitness theory to humans. Evolutionary psychologists argue that some of these behaviors are caused by the mismatch between ancestral and modern conditions. This mismatch presents some difficulties for behavioral analysis.

A second subtlety in human behavioral biology is the human ability to override some short-term likes and dislikes. Presumably, many simpler organisms do whatever feels best at every moment, without any analysis of the consequences. Humans have an ability (genetically based) to project their actions forward, and, in some cases, choose a path that yields less short-term, direct gratification.

Evidence is presented that, despite these two features, human behavior is significantly genetically constrained. In most situations the data for genetic influence will be less compelling than in language acquisition. In these cases, there are a number of types of evidence that indicate important genetic constraints. These lines of evidence (discussed below in theory and example) are:

- Continuity with non-human species. It is possible to find homologous behavior in individual non-human primate species, or derive cross-species rules relating reproductive payoffs to behavior.

- Universality. Behaviors that are present in all human societies may be "cultural," but they are more likely to be biologically restricted than variable behaviors.

- Constraints on learning. Certain features are hard or impossible to teach. The underlying constraints are biological.

This section concludes with examples chosen to illustrate the utility of evolutionary thinking in the study of human behavior.

Human language as a paradigm for human behavior

Human language shows potentially infinite surface variation on top of an immutable genetic core. The universal species-typical language architecture develops along genetically determined lines in all humans without instruction.

All human languages follow a set of linguistic rules that Noam Chomsky (1959, 1968) labels a universal grammar. The fact that all human societies use the same structure was used as an early argument that language is "innate". But Stephen Pinker (1994) points out that universal traits are not necessarily biological. Pinker speculates (as part of an argument in which he concludes that language is innate) that language was invented, found to be useful, and then spread culturally throughout humanity. Consider that most human societies currently use electricity but this is certainly not an argument for an "electricity" gene.

Pinker provides a variety of evidence that language is indeed importantly constrained by genes. Children in all societies acquire particular linguistic traits at the same age. Interestingly, this is also true of deaf children who use sign language to communicate, including the "babbling" that characterizes one development stage. Children rapidly acquire the complex rules of the universal grammar without the need for any formal instruction.

Further evidence that language structure is innate is provided by the linguist Derek Bickerton (Bickerton, 1990; Pinker, 1994) in his studies of new language formation. A "pidgin" language results when the vocabulary of one culture is used in a grammar-free fashion by members of the second culture. Pidgins do not abide by the "universal grammar" of human language, but a transformation takes place when the second generation learns the new language. Children of pidgin speakers "injected grammatical complexity where none existed before, resulting in a brand-new, richly expressive language." In other words, children use the pidgin vocabulary and impose the universal grammar rules to create what is called a "creole".

The details of language, such as vocabulary, are culturally dependent. However, all humans possess the same underlying grammatical structure that develops without, or even in spite of, cultural transmission. Furthermore, the universal grammar of human language is one of several logically equivalent grammars. All humans use the same language structure because it is coded in our genes, not because this grammar is somehow inevitable or unique with regard to communication theory.

Evolutionary psychology and the EEA

Whereas traditional psychology describes the mind, evolutionary psychology explores the Darwinian roots and consequences of mental structures. Evolutionary psychology has deep intellectual roots including Darwin's adaptationist view of behavior and was first laid out at length by E.O. Wilson and Charles Lumsden. (Lumsden and Wilson, 1981; Lumsden and Wilson, 1983). The field, as described in *The Adapted Mind* by Barkow, Tooby and Cosmides (1992), has three main premises:

a) There is a universal, genetic human nature consisting of a set of problem-solving mechanisms.

b) These genetic mechanisms are best viewed as "adaptations," i.e., they evolved to solve problems in ancestral environments.

c) The problems that these genetic adaptations solve, are not those of the modern, industrial world. Rather, they are the problems faced by hunter-gathering humans in the late Pleistocene epoch.

33

The Environment of Evolutionary Adaptiveness (EEA)

Human genes are probably not in equilibrium with modern industrial conditions. The argument against equilibrium contrasts the rates of societal and genetic change. Human ancestors spent 2 million years as Pleistocene hunter-gatherers. Earlier non-hominid ancestors existed as foragers for several hundred million years. Modern humans, *Homo sapiens sapiens*, arose approximately 180,000 years ago. The invention of agriculture took place roughly 10,000 years ago, and modern industrial society began within the last 200 years (Tooby and Cosmides, 1990).

The exact rate of genetic change varies, and gene frequencies shift substantially within 1,000 years (Lumsden and Wilson, 1981), but it is reasonable to believe that most genes have changed little in the last 10,000 years. Inter-species data indicate that genes change very slowly. Human and chimpanzee lines diverged approximately five million years ago yet by some measures (Luke and Verma, 1995) still share 98% of their DNA. Furthermore, certain gene sequences are functionally identical in bacteria and humans, indicating conservation over hundreds of millions of years.

One example that provides information about the speed of human genetic evolution concerns the ability of adults to digest milk. Infants in species that lactate can convert the milk sugar lactose into useful energy. Adults in these species usually cannot digest lactose, a loss without consequence since they do not consume milk. The reproductive payoffs changed for humans with the domestication of animals and the presence of milk throughout the entire lifespan. In this context, an adult ability to digest lactose would presumably confer selective advantage. A study (McCracken, 1971) shows that humans from the parts of the world that domesticated animals earliest have systematically higher adult ability to digest lactose. However, some adults, in all populations, are "lactose-intolerant" indicating that this fairly simple genetic change has not run to completion in thousands of years.

If human genes have changed little in the last 10,000 years, and if human behavioral genes are adaptations to solve specific problems, then they are the problems faced by foraging humans. The term "environment of evolutionary adaptiveness," or EEA, is used to describe the time between the origin of modern humans and the adoption of agriculture. The assumption is that many important features of the ecological environment remained constant during this period allowing human genes to reach equilibrium. The period from 1.8 million years ago up to 10,000 years ago is called the Pleistocene epoch. Thus, the short-hand phrase used by evolutionary psychologists is that humans are "Pleistocene hunter-gatherers".

An article by John Tooby and Leda Cosmides (1990) highlights several key features of the EEA. Humans existed in small (hundreds of individuals at most) groups of relatives living in low population density. The primary modes of food acquisition were hunting and gathering, without domestication of animals or agriculture. The inter-species selective pressure included predator avoidance and mechanisms for resource acquisition. Intra-group competition existed over depletable resources and reproductive opportunities.

Hunter-gatherers in an alien world? On the endogeneity of culture.

A legitimate question to ask is, how do our EEA adapted brains function in today's "alien" environment? Taking any species from an ancient evolutionary niche to an arbitrary environment is likely to produce extremely maladaptive behavior. How do humans, equipped with hunter-gatherer bodies and minds, sometimes manage to get through the day without warfare, depression, sickness and death?

The answer comes from realizing that, although the modern environment is very different from the EEA, it is not *arbitrarily* different. Human societal structures are endogenous to human genes, which is to say that cultural evolution is constrained by human nature. There are infinitely many ways to organize human society and presumably most of them would result in chaos. This is precisely why human behavioral biology has predictive power. For example, no dense human population functions today without some version of law enforcement. Law and law enforcement become necessary because the mental mechanisms that prevent societally destructive behavior in small human groups break down once the population exceeds a threshold. Thus, we can confidently predict that any functioning human society with high population density will also have police. Similar predictions can be made for a long list of societal characteristics.

Theodosius Dobzhansky[4] describes the endogeneity of culture as follows: "in a sense, human genes have surrendered their primacy in human evolution to an entirely new, nonbiological or superorganic agent, culture. However, it should not be forgotten

---

[4] As quoted on page 21 of E.O. Wilson's *On Human Nature*

that this agent is entirely dependent on the human genotype." From this perspective the language homology should be clear. Within the constraints set by the human genome, culture in its many manifestations is free to choose from an infinite set. In other words, the plasticity of human behavior is a genetically programmed plasticity.

Implications for human behavioral biology

Evolutionary psychology argues that human behavioral biology will remain an art. The specifics of the EEA are important for understanding what mechanisms were likely to arise, and many critical environmental features are unknown. Furthermore, even if the EEA were completely described, evolution is path-dependent. When there are multiple solutions to a particular problem, evolutionary theory provides little insight as to which solution will arise.

In spite of these difficulties, it is possible to describe the general properties of behavior that arose by natural selection. Theory predicts that humans may be very good at solving evolutionarily relevant problems. For example, humans were group hunters for at least several hundred thousand years. That lifestyle requires efficient cooperation which in turn requires sophisticated mental accounting to reduce cheating and free-riding. Recent psychological studies (discussed in detail below) suggest that all humans have specific mental machinery necessary for solving this important and ancient problem.

In contrast, evolutionary theory predicts that humans may respond to novel situations in a manner that appears ineffective or irrational. Evolutionary processes converge slowly at best, and many generations are required to produce elegant solutions.

In this light, it is not surprising that innate human mechanisms are not adapted to deal with evolutionary novelties such as heroin and readily available dietary fat.

This evolutionary view of brain design stands in contrast to other approaches. At one extreme stands the neo-classical economic model, which assumes that people use the same, sophisticated general-purpose process to solve all problems. While there is considerable empirical support for the neoclassical model of behavior, there is also evidence that humans do not effectively analyze some very simple situations. This failure is used by some to argue that the neoclassical model should be discarded. A natural selection perspective resolves the apparent paradox by predicting that people will have advanced mechanisms for some problems, but perform poorly in other logically similar, but evolutionarily different, situations.

The society of mind and human discipline

Odysseus returning home from the Trojan war wanted to hear the Siren song. Foreseeing that the sound would seduce him into destroying his ship, he had himself tied to the mast, ordered his crew to put wax in their ears, and thus became the first person to hear the music of the Sirens and survive. The human ability to forecast and manipulate desires, though limited, appears to be unmatched in other species.

Until fairly recently, economists modeled firms as discrete, profit-maximizing entities. Agency theory (see Jensen and Meckling, 1976 for an early article) decomposes the firm by considering the individuals and their payoffs. The theory of the human brain has undergone a similar process. Originally modeled as a cohesive unit, Freud introduced the agency theory of the mind by positing superego, ego and id as separate, and sometimes

38

conflicting, entities. The number of mental agents was expanded by several people into what Marvin Minsky (1986) calls a "society of mind".

When viewed from a society of mind perspective, the human ability to override certain desires can be viewed as a supervisory mental agent. This presence of the "discipline" agent makes the study of instinctual behavior more difficult, but it does not mean that humans lack the special purpose agents apparent in other species. This view of the human brain differs from that of standard economics. Whereas economics posits a general purpose problem solving machinery, the agency view has a number of special purpose algorithms with general rationality superimposed.

The term "instinct" is used by several researchers in Stephen Pinker (1994) to describe some behavior. What is the difference between instinctual and non-instinctual behavior? By instinct Pinker means a behavior that is developed by almost all humans in most environments. In the case of language, only a small percentage of people lacks the genetic material for development. Similarly, only extreme deprivation of human contact prevents the acquisition of language. As a result, almost all humans have exactly the same language behavior at a fundamental level.

Non-instinctual traits, according to Pinker, are those that are difficult to acquire, or which require relatively rare environments. In particular, the mastery of these traits often requires the use of general purpose reasoning to override, or otherwise modify, the underlying special mechanisms. For example, running marathons requires perseverance in spite of pain, and learning calculus depends on classroom instruction and textbooks.

The ability to refrain from spending money has the characteristics of a non-instinctual behavior, in that it is highly variable, difficult to learn, and rare. A model

39

consistent with the observed absence of liquid financial wealth is that humans have no conscious, instinctual discount rate. The special purpose agents dispose humans to consume all food (or other commodities) on a given day, and to "invest" the surplus in kin and friends. Surplus calories are stored in the individual's fat cells, in the bodies of other individuals with shared genetic material, and in reciprocal favors owed. This method does not require explicit savings, and may have been the only savings technology in the EEA.

In the presence of modern savings tools, there are reasons to save, but only a small percentage of people, with strong discipline agents, is able to resist spending liquid financial assets. Some resist by playing games with themselves to save without any readily available resources (Laibson, 1993), and others do not voluntarily save. The result is that the vast majority of people have no readily available spending power.

Evidence supporting the main assumptions of human behavioral biology

Humans are unique in several ways as described above. Nevertheless, evidence along several lines suggests that humans exist at one extreme of a biological spectrum, not as a species completely separated from others.

Behavioral continuity with non-human species

The search for human uniqueness has led researchers to list features not found in other species. As our awareness of other species, particularly non-human primates, grows, many of these "human" traits have been revealed to be shared. This section argues that a cross-species perspective can inform the study of human behavior in two ways. The first is by examination of our very close genetic relatives, the non-human primates. The second is by looking across all species for robust relationships between reproductive

40

payoffs and behavior. The common origins of behavior should not be particularly surprising given the similarity between humans and some other species in physiology and brain design. This similarity allows pharmaceutical products, including those designed to alter human mental states, to be productively tested on non-human species.

A systematic comparison of humans and 15 other primate species is performed in an article (Rodseth et al., 1991) entitled "The Human Community as a Primate Society." On a wide range of attributes designed to be "species neutral," the authors conclude that human societies are "... peculiar compared to other primate societies. At the same time, however, certain aspects of human sociality resemble those of a few other primates..." (p 222)

Chimpanzees are humans' closest living relative, and are of particular relevance to the study of non-human homologues. Genetic analysis confirms that humans and chimps are more closely related than chimps are to gorillas. (Lewin, 1987; Ruvolo et al., 1994) One well-known chimp behavior is the use of more than a dozen types of primitive tools (see Boesch, 1993 for a recent review). Chimps have non-reproductive heterosexual sex (while pregnant for example), and homosexual sex (Wrangham, 1993). Frans de Waal (1982) describes a primate society filled with a variety of complex relationships in *Chimpanzee Politics: Power and Sex Among Apes.*

Chimpanzees form coalitions in pursuit of intra- and inter-species goals. Chimp parties cooperatively stalk, kill and eat other types of animals (Boesch and Boesch, 1989; Stanford, 1995). These coalitions also conduct intergroup aggression (Goodall, 1986; Manson and Wrangham, 1991) where males patrol territorial borders and use advantageous situations to attack neighbors. In a review article, Richard Wrangham

41

(1987, p 66) states: "At both sites [Kasoge, Tanzania and Gombe, Tanzania] intercommunity interactions are almost invariably hostile. At Gombe the deaths of five adult males and one adult female appeared to be the direct result of severe attacks seen to be made by males from a neighboring community..."

While chimps can shed light on the origins of a variety of human behaviors, other work will be informed by looking across species. One example has to do with gender roles and mate attraction. Krebs and Davies (1984) document a rule that the sex that invests more in offspring is the sex that is courted. The logic is clear. The large investment made by one sex is a valuable reproductive asset that is sought by the other sex. In mammals, female gestation and lactation drive this relationship so males court females. In other species where the investment is done by males the roles are reversed. Krebs and Davies describe a study (Petrie, 1983) in moorhens as follows: "... males do almost three-quarters of the incubation and females play an active role in competing for the chance to mate with good incubators. These ideal husbands are small and fat ..." It is simply impossible to discover such relationships by looking at a single species.

So human warfare and some aspects of gender roles may have genetic origins. Some critics of sociobiology argue that statements about genetic roots provide moral support to practitioners of offensive behaviors. These critics are making a fundamental logical error. Determining the "naturalness" of something has no bearing whatsoever on its desirability. Hurricanes, AIDS, and cancer are all natural and bad. Knowledge of genetic origins can help eliminate undesired behaviors. For example, understanding the instinctual causes of violence can help structure a society where these tendencies are suppressed or channeled into socially acceptable outlets.

42

Human universals

All humans share certain behaviors. Two examples are described here. (See Brown, 1991 for a more thorough treatment.)

Human facial expressions and their interpretation are universal. Ekman (1973) reports on studies where individuals are asked to classify photographs from other cultures. All people correctly identity cross-cultural facial expressions representing emotions including fear, anger, disgust, surprise and happiness. This includes societies that have been isolated for thousands of years. The human smile, and its interpretation, are part of the human genome.

In similar studies, humans show cross-cultural color appreciation. All humans divide colors into the same groups. In this case, the behavior is driven by the physiology of color detectors in the human eye. Because all humans share the same color receptor genes, they classify colors in the same fashion.

Humans and cheater-detectors: behavior that is genetically moderated

Cosmides and Tooby (1992) provide evidence that human brains solve evolutionarily relevant problems significantly better than other logically identical problems. The studies concern the ability of humans to detect people who are cheating in relationships. A "social exchange" situation is one where a benefit is earned only by paying some related costs. For example, accepting part of a neighbor's food today may, as part of an explicit or implicit social contract, require future reciprocation. Evolutionary theory predicts that, in species that engage in social exchange, there is strong selective pressure to avoid being cheated, which requires the identification of cheating.

What defines a cheater in social exchange? A cheater is someone who obtains the benefits without paying the associated costs. Logically, the problem structure is to evaluate the truth of the statement $P \rightarrow Q$ where P means "obtained the benefit" and Q means "paid the cost." Subjects' ability is tested by telling the subjects that there are four groups of people in a social exchange setting: People who took the benefit (P), those who did not take the benefit (not P), those who paid the cost (Q) , and those who did not pay the cost (not Q). The subjects are asked which groups might contain cheaters on the social contract.

The correct answer is that only the groups that received the benefit or did not pay the cost could possibly have cheated. To evaluate $P \rightarrow Q$ requires checking the value of Q in the cases where P is true, and checking the value of P when Q is false. So the correct algorithm for efficiently finding cheaters consists of i) checking the group that received benefits for individuals who did not pay costs <u>and</u> ii) checking the group that did not pay costs for people who received benefits. There is no need to investigate the groups that paid costs or that did not receive benefits.

Tooby and Cosmides find that people can evaluate the $P \rightarrow Q$ statement in the context of detecting cheaters, but not in other contexts. The findings are robust (highly statistically significant) across a variety of cultures, subject groups and exact problem description. The following is a detailed description of one of the experiments.

The subjects are given a verbal description of a situation and then asked how they would determine if a violation had occurred. The cheater-detector version states that hungry people arrive on a Pacific, but warlike, island. They are greeted by a chief that offers to feed them after they have been tattooed into his tribe. The trouble is that other

44

tribes kill tattoo wearers, and, furthermore, the chief has been known to withhold food even after tattoos are performed. The subjects are asked which of the following four groups need to be examined to determine if the chief has cheated on the bargain: tattoo wearers, non-tattoo wearers, hungry travelers, fed travelers. 74% of subjects correctly stated that determining if the chief cheated only requires checking i) if tattoo wearers were fed, and ii) if hungry travelers have tattoos.

A second group of subjects is asked to look for altruistic behavior by the chief. The "altruistic" version is almost identical to the cheater-detector with only one sentence changed. Instead of warning that the chief has a history of cheating, subjects are told that the chief sometimes acts generously by feeding without tattooing. Again the subjects are asked to identify which groups need to be examined to detect the chief's behavior which this time is altruism. In a variety of subject groups no more than 40% correctly stated that determining if the chief acted altruistically only requires checking i) if tattooless individuals received food, and ii) if fed travelers have tattoos.

The conclusion is that detecting cheaters was a problem faced in the EEA and detecting altruists was not. Therefore, humans have a mental adaptation to solve the problem faced in the EEA that is extremely context dependent.

Examples of human behavioral biology

Israeli marriage data

Joseph Shepher (1971) conducted a study of sexual relationships and marriage within Israeli kibutzim. Among more that 2,000 documented marriages not one was between individuals who had spent more than 2 years together in the years between birth

45

and age six. Furthermore, there was not a single reported case of heterosexual activity within these groups. These findings are surprising because proximity is usually the best predictor of sexual relations. Furthermore, there were no cultural prohibitions against sex or marriage.

The explanation for this behavior lies in a subconscious evolutionary mechanism to avoid incest. Mating with close relatives increases the likelihood that recessive deleterious genes will be expressed. One study (Morton et al., 1956) of American and French populations estimates that each person carries an average of four lethal gene equivalents. Thus, incest carries heavy costs and there is selective pressure for a mechanism to favor sex with non-kin.

Examination of the Israeli data reveals that the individuals involved were raised in group nurseries. The study concludes that humans are not sexually attracted to others with whom they interacted with during critical childhood periods. This instinctual mechanism works in some environments, presumably included the EEA, to prevent incest. (See also Wolf, 1995 for a more recent study of incest avoidance.)

Seeking social information

A more speculative arena for evolutionary insight is explored by Jerome Barkow (1992), who asks why we collect social information on strangers. The phenomenon to explain is the obsession with events such as the O.J. Simpson murder trial. Perhaps even more odd is the retention of information on characters in TV soap operas. Although soap opera characters are known to be fictional, many people devote considerable effort to keep up on the latest development in their favorite characters' imaginary lives.

The origin of this behavior, Barkow argues, lies in two facts. First, intra-group social information is extremely important. Whether in the EEA, or in a modern environment, the health, disposition, and reproductive status of group members have obvious strategic effects on each other. This implies that social knowledge can be useful. Second, the concept of a stranger is an environmental novelty. Simply put, social information about everyone was important in the EEA, so humans never developed a classification system based on likely future interaction. After all, O.J. Simpson is sitting in people's living room, albeit on TV. The underlying psychological mechanisms assume that he is part of the social group, and begin amassing information.

Heroin and the consumption of dietary fat.

Drug use and the consumption of dietary fat can be understood in an evolutionary framework. The body has a general mechanism for reinforcement of certain behaviors. This "do-it-again" center is fired by certain stimuli and results in behavior to obtain the good feeling again.

In the EEA, dietary fat was a scarce and valuable commodity, thus the body evolved to place a high reward on its acquisition. This reward takes a very specific form. Fat molecules fit precisely into receptors in the mouth, which starts a cascade of events leading to pleasure. Near the end of this cascade is the release of certain neurotransmitters that produce the positive feeling. In an evolutionary environment, this system works to advantage as individuals exert high effort to obtain and consume highly valuable dietary fat.

47

Two modern phenomena alter the historic relationships to the detriment of human happiness. First, the effort required to obtain dietary fat has been reduced substantially. The same drives that produce healthy behavior in the EEA lead us to want to consume fat in levels that dramatically shorten lifespan. If human genes were in equilibrium with today's environment, dry brown rice would presumably taste better than a Big Mac. A person may choose to avoid dietary fat, but cannot change the physical wiring that produces neurotransmitters when fat is placed in the mouth.

The second modern phenomenon is the direct introduction of chemicals to stimulate neuronal firing. Heroin, and other drugs, produce their effects by hooking into the pleasure pathway. After a heroin injection, the "do-it-again" center is fired and the individual is motivated to repeat the behavior. As with fat, individuals can choose not to perform the activity, but they cannot alter the biochemistry.

Conclusion

Human behavioral biology has unique features not present in the other study of non-human species. Proponents of genetic roots to human behavior are often caricatured as condemning humans to robotically carrying out programmed tasks. The truth is that genes allow considerable freedom within constraints.

Review of economic literature

Introduction

Paul Samuelson (1986) wrote: "There is much territory between economics and biology that is still virgin ground. It will be tilled increasingly in the future. We should not be surprised if the first explorations are both crude and pretentious. Wisdom and maturity are the last settlers to arrive in pioneering communities."

A number of economists are applying evolutionary thinking to microeconomic foundations with a sophistication that exceeds Samuelson's prediction. However, there is not a comprehensive framework in the economic literature, and the number of articles is fairly low. This section summarizes the articles that deal with the genetic component of preferences. It does not address the larger economic literature on cultural evolution such as Armen Alchian's work (1950) or that of Nelson and Winter (1982).

The section is divided into one methodological area and three applications: altruism, risk, and intertemporal trade-offs. The methodological point is the idea that human emotions generally, and utility in particular, can be viewed as evolutionary adaptations. This general concept is covered in more detail in the evolutionary psychology section, and its particular application to utility is explained in the genetic perspective on economics section. The shorter version is contained here to provide a more cohesive discussion of the economics literature, and a compact set of references.

Each section begins with the 'mainstream' prediction from natural science that organisms act 'as if' they seek to maximize reproductive success. The word mainstream is used in quotations to indicate that natural science thinking is not monolithic on any of these points. Thus, while only one natural science position is listed in each section below the interested reader is encouraged to investigate further.

Emotions are tools to induce behavior

Natural Science

From the perspective of evolutionary survival, the internal states of an individual are relevant only insofar as they have reproductive consequences. Thus, happiness, anger, fear, disgust, and the whole range of human emotions (and presumably those of other species) are products of natural selection to the extent, **and only to the extent**, that they alter behaviors with fitness effects.

The application of this view to non-human species has a long history. Darwin was important to its development by incorporating humans into the scheme, and by publishing *The Expression of Emotion in Man and Animal.* (Darwin, 1873)

More recently, this view has founded the field of evolutionary psychology that asks "why are emotions?" instead of the traditional psychological question of "what are emotions?" *The Adapted Mind* (Barkow et al., 1992) is a scholarly collection of articles applying evolutionary psychology to a range of topics from social conventions to aesthetic judgments.

Economics

What does evolutionary psychology have to say about the economic concept of utility? In short, that "utility" is a means to a reproductive end. In the scientific framework, utility maximization can be viewed as a mechanism to promote reproductive success.

Gary Becker (1976) appears to be the first to make the link explicit by writing: "The preferences taken as given by economists and vaguely attributed to 'human nature' or something similar ... may be largely explained by the selection over time of traits having greater genetic fitness and survival value."

Jack Hirshleifer wrote two early papers (1977, 1978) where he expresses the view that emotions are tricks played upon us by our genes. Schelling (1978) observes that emotions can be viewed as commitment devices in strategic situations. Robert Frank (1988) greatly expands on Schelling's theme, viewing a wide range of emotions as self-interested adaptations. Vernon Smith, Elizabeth Hoffman, and Kevin McCabe have published several articles (see, for example, Hoffman et al., 1996) that incorporate concepts from evolutionary psychology into an economic framework.

Hansson and Stuart (1990) formalize Becker's insight by considering what sort of utility function will emerge from a Darwinian process. They find an equilibrium relationship between marginal utilities and reproductive consequences. Specifically, for any two goods the equilibrium ratio of marginal utilities will equal the ratio of marginal fitness contributions. Thus, when the individual solves the traditional utility maximization problem he or she is "as if" solving a fitness maximization problem.

Binmore (1994, p 151) poses this as a principal-agent problem with genes as principals and individuals as agents. He asserts that preferences and choice mechanisms arose as adaptations for uncertain environments. Because the agent will have better information, and the principal "knows" this, the principal delegates, but controls indirectly through the incentive scheme of preferences. Waldman (1994) takes the adaptationist line one step further by arguing that even systematic mistakes can be viewed as adaptations to evolutionary environments.

Altruism and selfishness

Natural Science

Voluntary acts that diminish an individual's payoff seem inconsistent with a theory of maximal replication. However, apparently altruistic acts are observed in every human society, and in a wide variety of non-human species. This presents a challenge to evolutionary theory as evidenced by E.O. Wilson's[5] question: "How can altruism, which by definition reduces personal fitness, possibly evolve by natural selection?"

Natural science has dealt with this by assuming that altruism does not exist, and viewing acts that appear altruistic are being only part of the story. The altruistic behaviors are combined with selfish behaviors so that the summation over the linked acts is positive. The selfish acts that accompany altruistic acts can be found by looking at other copies of the actor's genes (*kin selection*), by looking at repeated interactions (*reciprocal altruism*), and by examining selfish acts that appear identical to the actor (*manipulation*).

Kin Selection: The gene is the relevant evolutionary replicating unit, not the individual and not the group. W.D. Hamilton's 1964 paper lays the mathematical foundation for this idea which has become famous under the rubric of Richard Dawkins' *The Selfish Gene* (Dawkins, 1976).

Reciprocal Altruism: The second mechanism is that of reciprocal altruism (Trivers, 1971) where apparently selfless acts are expected do be repaid with interest.

---

[5] *Sociobiology*, p.3. abridged version

Manipulation: To understand this third class consider the case of birds that feed the young of other species. Cuckoos are labeled "brood parasites" because they lay their eggs in other birds' nests to the benefit of cuckoo genes (Payne, 1977). Why do the host birds feed the young cuckoos? The answer is that host birds have not evolved a mechanism to differentiate their own young from cuckoo young. Thus, the hosts can only stop feeding the cuckoos by starving their own offspring. This is labeled manipulation because the recipient receives favors by fooling the "altruist" through mimicry.

Economics

Kin selection: Economists joined the debate on kin selection soon after the publication of E.O. Wilson's *Sociobiology*, and sought not only economic applications but also to contribute to the natural science literature. Gordon Tullock (1978a, b) wrote "Using economic theory of public goods, this article demonstrates that kin selection cannot be used to explain altruism outside of the direct parent-child link." Another economist Frech (1978) responds directly to Tullock saying that if resources are scarce (as they must be) then "... Tullock's results are simply wrong." Paul Samuelson (1983) argues that kin selection is valid then generalizes Hamilton's theory to include shared genetic material in individuals who are not relatives.

There is a group of scientists led by Wynne-Edwards (1986) and D.S. Wilson (Wilson and Sober, 1994) that contends, under certain conditions, natural selection occurs at the group level. Proponents of this view argue that groups performing efficient, altruistic acts will have higher average replication rates than selfish groups, thus altruistic behavior will flourish. Samuelson (1993) presents a model that supports the group selection point of view.

Reciprocal Altruism: Economists have adopted, and generalized, Triver's insight. The core of these ideas is contained in the repeated games literature. Various folk theorems indicate that a very broad range of behaviors is consistent with individual maximization. (See Fudenberg and Tirole, 1993, particularly chapters 5 and 9 for a summary.)

One variant of the repeated interaction framework considers the behavior of egoists in a world with some altruists. Becker (1976) and Bergstrom (Bergstrom and Stark, 1993) show that in a world with some altruists (the existence of these altruists is not explained), egoists may be rewarded for acting like altruists.

Manipulation: Herbert Simon (1993) argues that boundedly rational organisms are susceptible to altruistic manipulations. These organisms gain valuable information from others so they are willing to alter their behavior based on messages. In equilibrium some of these messages will, Simon argues, induce altruistic acts. In this view altruism is a form of taxation. An individual cannot gain the benefits of social knowledge without contributing to the public good.

Risk

Natural Science

The biological prediction is that evolution will favor behavior that maximizes expected replication rates. In other words, it predicts that organisms will be risk neutral over fitness units. Risk neutrality over fitness units implies risk-averse behavior over

54

goods with diminishing returns, and risk-seeking behavior towards goods with increasing returns.

Consider a traditional commodity such as corn. For a variety of reasons it is reasonable to expect the relationship between corn and reproduction to show decreasing returns. The first bushel of corn means much more than the one hundredth. A gamble that replaces one sure unit of corn for a fifty percent chance of two units of corn is an expected fitness losing gamble. Thus, inclusive fitness theory predicts risk-aversion towards commodities with decreasing returns.

The logic is reversed for goods with increasing returns. For example, assume that "status" has increasing returns in at least part of the distribution. In other words, assume people near the top of some status ranking such as kings and queens have dramatically better circumstances than those just a few rungs down. In this case "fair" gambles over status will increase expected fitness, and the theory predicts the evolution of risk-seeking behavior.

Economics

The standard economic assumption about risk differs in two ways from the biological. First, attitudes towards risk are taken as exogenous. Second, individuals are assumed to have the same risk attitude towards all commodities.

There are several economic papers that consider biologically derived risk attitudes. Rubin and Paul (1979) speculate that poor males might be below some minimum threshold for marriage and progeny. For these individuals, negative expected value bets can increase the expected reproductive success. Karni and Schmeidler (1986) propose that risk attitudes reflect the evolutionary goal of maximizing the probability of survival.

Arthur Robson has investigated several aspects of endogenous risk-attitudes. Robson (1992) finds that if relative wealth enters directly into utility func/tions then this will provide a "natural explanation for the 'concave-convex-concave' utility described by Friedman and Savage (Friedman and Savage, 1948)." Robson (1994a) assumes that the offspring per unit of wealth function shows increasing returns (for some males) and predicts risk-seeking behavior for them. Robson (1994b) finds that the optimal risk attitudes will depend on whether the risk is systematic or non-systematic.

Intertemporal allocations

Natural science

A standard explanation for positive discount rates is that humans are always at risk of dying. Both scientists and economists have worked to make this relationship explicit. Biologists have concluded that the maximization of inclusive fitness will lead to a species-dependent optimal rate of senescence and death. The original evolutionary insights into senescence were provided by Medawar (1946, 1952) discussed in detail by Williams (1957) and generalized by Hamilton (1966).

Current theory (Charlesworth, 1994, chapter 5 in particular) states that optimal intertemporal allocations will depend upon a number of factors, including the probability of survival, the age-dependent rate of reproduction, and the rate of population growth. This natural science literature does not convert easily into an economist's version of a discount rate. However two observations (similar to those in the risk section) can be

56

made. First, in principle, it is possible to derive optimal, intertemporal allocations from parameters such as mortality and reproduction rates. Second, the optimal discount rate will vary depending on commodity type.

Economics

Paul Samuelson (1958) concludes that "Every geometrically growing consumption-loan economy has an equilibrium market rate of interest exactly equal to its biological percentage growth rate." Becker and Mulligan (1993) study how rational people who "excessively" discount the future attempt to overcome their natural discount rate. Anthropologist Alan Rogers (1994) derives optimal discount rates from population parameters and concludes, in part, that rates should vary over an individual's lifetime.

Genetic perspective on economics

Introduction

This section proposes a methodology for genetic evolutionary economics that differs from traditional economic theory in two significant ways. First, while individuals may be very concerned with "utility", the underlying mental structures are assumed to have evolved to maximize reproductive success, not happiness. Second, the evolutionary approach assumes that the brain consists of problem-solving machinery for an ancestral world. These two evolutionary assumptions are integrated into a traditional economic process of definition, solution, prediction, empirical testing, re-examination of theory, etc.

The first portion of this section speculates on the adaptive advantage of having a concept of utility. Presumably simple organisms' behavior is directly programmed.

Somewhere in our evolutionary past the genes that encode for a perception of free will and for emotions arose. The adaptive assumption is that "emotional" organisms prospered because of some selective advantage conferred by the combination of perceived free will and internal mental states.

Regardless of evolutionary origin, human emotions exist. Given their existence, selective pressure exists upon the genetic component of emotions and their economic manifestation as preferences. The evolutionary question then becomes what sort of preferences will out reproduce their rivals.

Utility and utility maximization as adaptations

Giving individuals a sense of free will may increase reproductive success by allowing highly contingent strategies. If we start with the assumption that genes are omnipotent, but not omniscient this motivation becomes apparent. Presumably human genes could (at least at one point evolutionarily) encode behavior that is completely pre-programmed. However, the reproductive payoffs to behaviors are highly dependent on the state of the environment. Hunting might be productive in days with game present, honey acquisition profitable at certain times of the year, etc.

Consider, by analogy, the relationship between a corporate board of directors and the chief executive officer. Nothing forces the board to delegate control to the CEO, and a contract specifying exact duties could be written. However, a self-interested board balances the rewards delegation brings in the form of flexible, rapid CEO response with the cost of allowing the CEO exercise of his or her personal agenda. Similarly, the human emotional structure affords tremendous behavioral flexibility, but also enables reproductively costly acts such as suicide and voluntary sterilization.

What is the contingent strategy to obtain maximum reproductive success? In specific this is hard to describe, but two general traits might be expected. First, delegation to the organism via preferences should be driven by informational issues. In domains where the optimal behavior is invariant there should be no delegation. Second, once delegation has occurred some coordination mechanism may be useful.

Consider the case of non-contingent strategies. Humans have an entire set of important behaviors that are invariant to an individual's preferences. Perhaps most notable

59

in this area is the autonomous nervous system that controls many body functions. A fitness maximizing strategy always includes a beating heart so there is no need to include pulse in human preferences. Similar logic explains the absence of pain generators in most of the human brain. Pain is part of a system to modify behavior. There is no reproductive value to pain in uniformly fatal events, and in the EEA most head splittings resulted in death.

Once an organism has adopted a contingent strategy a concept of "utility" can coordinate behavior. While explicitly programming a highly contingent strategy is possible in principle, it is difficult because it requires specifying behavior for a large number of contingencies. Such a top-down approach can be compared with a Soviet style command economy.

In contrast to a command brain, our actual brain acts like a decentralized market economy with utility as the unit of exchange. As with a traditional market economy, there are prices associated with goods. Moving a leg may cost 3 utils, while entering a dark passageway 200 utils. At times various mental agents may be in conflict, and in the command brain some priority rule would be necessary. However, the decentralized brain allows competing agents to "bid" utility for the desired outcome. This system can be manipulated because agents do not have budget constraints. A rogue mental agent can win any bid by producing large amounts of neurotransmitters. However, the penalty for inefficient bidding, as defined by reproductive consequences, is extinction.

Darwinian utility functions

Given that preferences exist and that some choice mechanism exists, what can be said about the nature of these preferences? In the short term (their lifetimes), humans can be assumed to maximize happiness without concern for the reproductive consequences of their action, but an evolutionary accountant lurks just off stage keeping score of every move.

Natural selection will favor those preferences that induce the highest reproductive success. In equilibrium, preferences converge to those that induce behavior that is locally optimal as measured by fitness payoffs. The psychic utility of a commodity will reflect both its reproductive benefit and cost. More specifically, in equilibrium, the ratio of marginal utilities = ratio of marginal fitnesses = ratio of costs. (See Hansson and Stuart, 1990 for a derivation.) Note that humans in the EEA presumably faced costs measured in time, not dollars.

A second prediction is that commodities without fitness implications should have no effect on utility. Any positive utility from such commodities would spur wasteful seeking behavior, and any negative utility would spur equally wasteful avoidance behavior.

A third prediction is that preferences do not need to conform to any notion of consistency. *A priori* there is nothing to prevent genes from encoding time inconsistent preferences, and, of course, reaping the associated reproductive payoffs. It is perhaps harder to understand why genes cannot achieve their goals without resorting to inconsistent preferences. Nevertheless, when it is in their interest, genes can encode for preference shifts such as forgetting the pain of child birth.

61

Finally, evolutionary theory makes no prediction about human happiness, even for individuals who are relatively successful in achieving the illusory goals inspired by utility. The theory predicts only that surviving utility functions induced replication better than the utility functions that they defeated. *Ceteris paribus*, the gene might just as well allow the organism some utility. However, if happiness comes at the expense of replication, the gene will always choose replication. In the words of Leda Cosmides and John Tooby: "It doesn't need to make one happy, it doesn't need to maximize subjective utility, it doesn't need to promote the survival of the species, it doesn't need to promote social welfare. To be selected for, it need only promote its own replication better than alternative designs." (Cosmides and Tooby, 1992, p 172)

Building genetic evolutionary economic models

Genetic evolutionary models start by assuming that preferences evolved to induce fitness maximizing behavior in the EEA. The steps beyond this stage are similar to traditional economic models. A few more comments follow here, but the argument is perhaps best understood by looking at chapter 3 of this thesis, where a genetic evolutionary model is developed.

The art in these models lies in finding evolutionarily relevant situations with stable relationships between proximate variables and reproductive success. Payoffs are written in fitness units and feasibility regions defined. The model is solved for fitness maximizing behavior in non-strategic situations, and for evolutionarily stable strategies when payoffs depend on others' action.

As discussed previously, humans do not have preferences over reproductive payoffs. Thus, a model that predicts fitness maximization is not useful by itself. To have meaningful results there must be some stable relationship between fitness and commodities that enter directly into preferences. Given such a relationship a genetic model will make testable predictions for human behavior. Such predictions can be compared to outcomes, new data can be gathered, and the traditional economic analysis cycle can proceed.

Concluding comments

Ever since Darwin evolutionary thinking has been usefully applied to a growing class of situations. A sophisticated understanding of evolutionary processes and consequences is routinely applied to human physiology and to non-human behavior. For example, we have no trouble understanding that big brains, opposable thumbs and appendixes were all selected evolutionarily, but in a modern environment big brains are crucial, thumbs important, and appendixes mainly trouble. More recently this type of analysis has begun to be applied to human behavior.

Economics has made great progress in developing a Cartesian system to analyze human behavior. The modern revolution in biology has natural application to the problems apparent in the axioms of the economic system, and the economic consequences of the biological revolution have not been explored. Economists who believe in a universal human nature are already implicit sociobiologists. It is time to make the relationship between genes and economic behavior explicit. The ultimate value of applying genetic evolutionary theory to economics cannot be known in advance, but the prospects appear bright.

Literature cited

Alchian, A. A. 1950. "Uncertainty, Evolution, and Economic Theory." *Journal of Political Economy* 58: 211-21.

Barkow, J. H. 1992. "Beneath New Culture is Old Psychology: Gossip and Social Stratification." in *The Adapted Mind: Evolutionary Psychology and the Generation of Culture*. J. H. Barkow, L. Cosmides and J. Tooby, Editors. New York: Oxford University Press: 627-638.

Barkow, J. H., L. Cosmides and J. Tooby, Editors. 1992. *The Adapted Mind: Evolutionary Psychology and the Generation of Culture*. New York: Oxford University Press.

Barro, R. 1974. "Are Government Bonds Net Wealth?" *Journal of Political Economy* 81: 1095-1117.

Becker, G. 1976. "Altruism, Egoism, and Genetic Fitness: Economics and Sociobiology." *Journal of Economic Literature* XIV(3): 817-826.

Becker, G. S. and C. B. Mulligan. 1993. "On the Endogenous Determination of Time Preference." *Unpublished Manuscript*.

Bergstrom, T. and O. Stark. 1993. "How Altruism can Prevail in an Evolutionary Environment." *American Economic Review* 83(2): 149-155.

Bernheim, D. 1987. "Ricardian Equivalence: An Evaluation of Theory and Evidence." in *NBER Macroeconomics Annual*: 263-303.

Bickerton, D. 1990. *Language & Species*. Chicago: University of Chicago Press.

Binmore, K. G. 1994. *Game Theory and the Social Contract*. Vol. 1: Playing Fair. Cambridge, Mass.: MIT Press.

Boesch, C. 1993. "Diversity of Tool Use and Tool-Making in Wild Chimpanzees." in *Use of Tools by Human and Non-human Primates*. Oxford: Clarendon Press: 158-168.

Boesch, C. and H. Boesch. 1989. "Hunting Behavior of Wild Chimpanzees in the Tai National Park." *American Journal of Physical Anthropology* 78: 547-73.

Brickman, P., D. Coates and R. J. Janoff-Bulman. 1978. "Lottery Winners and Accident Victims: Is Happiness Relative?" *Journal of Personality and Social Psychology* 36: 917-927.

Brown, D. E. 1991. *Human Universals*. Philadelphia: Temple University Press.

Charlesworth, B. 1994. *Evolution in Age-Structured Populations, second ed.* Cambridge, U.K.: Cambridge University Press.

Chomsky, N. 1959. "A Review of B.F. Skinner's 'Verbal Behavior'." *Language* 35: 26-58.

Chomsky, N. 1968. *Language and Mind*. New York: Harcourt, Brace & World.

Cosmides, L. and J. Tooby. 1992. "Cognitive Adaptations for Social Exchange." in *The Adapted Mind: Evolutionary Psychology and the Generation of Culture*. J. H.

Barkow, L. Cosmides and J. Tooby, Editors. New York: Oxford University Press: 163-228.

Daly, M. and M. Wilson. 1983. *Sex, Evolution, and Behavior.* Belmont, CA: Wadsworth Publishing Co.

Darwin, C. 1859. *On the Origin of Species by Means of Natural Selection, or the Preservation of Favoured Races in the Struggle for Life.* London: John Murray.

Darwin, C. 1873. *The Expression of the Emotions in Man and Animals.* New York: D. Appleton and Co.

Dawkins, R. 1976. *The Selfish Gene.* New York: Oxford University Press.

De Waal, F. B. M. 1982. *Chimpanzee Politics: Power and Sex among Apes.* London: Cape.

Diekstra, R. F. W. and N. Garnefski. 1995. "On the Nature, Magnitude, and Causality of Suicidal Behaviors: An International Perspective." *Suicide and Life-Threatening Behavior* 25(1): 36-58.

Diener, E. 1995. "Cross-Cultural Correlates of Life Satisfaction and Self-esteem." *Journal of Personality and Social Psychology* 68(4): 653-664.

Diener, E. 1995. "Happiness in Nations: Subjective Appreciation of Life in 56 Nations 1946-1992. (book review)." *Social Indicators Research* 35(1): 117-22.

Diener, E., E. Sandvik, L. Seidlitz and M. Diener. 1993. "The Relationship Between Income and Subjective Well-being: Relative or Absolute?" *Social Indicators Research* 28(3): 195-224.

Duesenberry, J. S. 1949. *Income, Saving, and the Theory of Consumer Behavior.* Cambridge: Harvard University Press.

Easterlin, R. 1974. "Does Economic Growth Improve the Human Lot?" in *Nations and Households in Economic Growth.* P. A. David and M. W. Reder, Editors. New York: Academic Press: 89-125.

Ekman, P. 1973. "Cross-Cultural Studies of Facial Expression." in *Darwin and Facial Expression: A Century of Research in Review.* P. Ekman, Editor. New York: Academic Press: 169-222.

Forsythe, R., J. L. Horowitz, N. E. Savin and M. Sefton. 1994. "Fairness in Simple Bargaining Experiments." *Games and Economic Behavior* 6(3): 347-69.

Frank, R. H. 1988. *Passions Within Reason.* New York: W. W. Norton & Company.

Frech, H. E. 1978. "Altruism, Malice, and Public Goods." *Journal of Social and Biological Structures* 1(2): 1881-85.

Friedman, M. 1953. *Essays in Positive Economics.* Chicago: University of Chicago Press.

Friedman, M. and L. Savage. 1948. "The Utility Analysis of Choices Involving Risk." *Journal of Political Economy* 56: 279-304.

Fudenberg, D. and J. Tirole. 1993. *Game Theory.* Cambridge, Massachusetts: The MIT Press.

Garcia, J. and R. Koelling. 1966. "The Relation of Cue to Consequence in Avoidance Learning." *Psychonomic Science*: 123-124.

Goodall, J. 1986. *The Chimpanzees of Gombe: Patterns of Behavior.* Cambridge, Mass.: Belknap Press of Harvard University Press.

Gould, S. J. and R. C. Lewontin. 1979. "The Spandrels of San Marco and the Panglossian Program: A Critique of the Adaptationist Programme." *Proceedings of the Royal Society of London* 205: 581-588.

Hamilton, W. D. 1964. "The Genetical Evolution of Social Behavior I and II." *Journal of Theoretical Biology* 7: 1-16, 17-52.

Hamilton, W. D. 1966. "The Moulding of Senescence by Natural Selection." *Journal of Theoretical Biology* 12(1): 12-45.

Hansson, I. and C. Stuart. 1990. "Malthusian Selection of Preferences." *American Economic Review* 80(3): 529-44.

Hirshleifer, J. 1977. "Economics from a Biological Perspective." *Journal of Law and Economics* 20: 1-52.

Hirshleifer, J. 1978. "Natural Economy vs. Political Economy." *Journal of Social and Biological Structures* October: 319-37.

Hoffman, E., K. McCabe and V. L. Smith. 1996. "Social Distance and Other-Regarding Behavior in Dictator Games." *American Economic Review* 86(3): 653.

Jensen, M. C. and W. H. Meckling. 1976. "Theory of the Firm: Managerial Behavior, Agency Costs, and Capital Structure." *Journal of Financial Economics* 3: 305-360.

Karni, E. and D. Schmielder. 1986. "Self-preservation as a Foundation of Rational Behavior under Risk." *Journal of Economic Behavior and Organization* 7: 71-82.

Keynes, J. M. 1972. "Economic Possibilities of Our Grandchildren." in *Essays in Persuasion.* London: Macmillan. **9:** 451.

Krebs, J. R. and N. B. Davies. 1984. *Behavioural Ecology: An Evolutionary Approach, 2nd ed.* Sunderland, Mass.: Sinauer Associates.

Laibson, D. I. 1993. "Golden Eggs and Hyperbolic Discounting." *MIT mimeo.*

Lewin, R. 1987. "My Close Cousin the Chimpanzee; Recent Evidence of Molecular Biology Indicates that Humans and Chimpanzees are Each Others' Closest Relative, a Conclusion that Remains at Odds with Most Anatomical Inferences." *Science* 238(4825): 273-276.

Luke, S. and R. S. Verma. 1995. "Human (Homo sapiens) and Chimpanzee (Pan troglodytes) Share Similar Ancestral Centromeric Alpha Satellite DNA Sequences but Other Fractions of Heterochromatin Differ Considerably." *American Journal of Physical Anthropology* 96(1): 63-72.

Lumsden, C. J. and E. O. Wilson. 1981. *Genes, Mind, and Culture: The Coevolutionary Process.* Cambridge, Mass.: Harvard University Press.

Lumsden, C. J. and E. O. Wilson. 1983. *Promethean Fire: Reflections on the Origin of the Mind.* Cambridge, Mass.: Harvard University Press.

Manson, J. H. and R. W. Wrangham. 1991. "Intergroup Aggression in Chimpanzees and Humans." *Current Anthropology* 32(4): 369-377.

Mas-Colell, A., M. D. Whinston and J. R. Green. 1995. *Microeconomic Theory.* New York: Oxford University Press.

Maynard Smith, J. 1982. *Evolution and the Theory of Games.* Cambridge: Cambridge University Press.

Maynard Smith, J. and G. R. Price. 1973. "The Logic of Animal Conflict." *Nature* 246(5427): 15-18.

McCracken, R. 1971. "Lactase Deficiency: An Example of Dietary Evolution." *Current Anthropology* 12: 479-517.

Medawar, P. B. 1946. "Old Age and Natural Death." *Modern Quarterly* 1: 30-56.

Medawar, P. B. 1952. *An Unsolved Problem of Biology.* London: H.K. Lewis.

Minsky, M. L. 1986. *The Society of Mind.* New York, N.Y.: Simon and Schuster.

Morton, N. E., J. F. Crow and H. J. Muller. 1956. "An Estimate of the Mutational Damage in Man from Data on Consanguineous Marriages." *Proceedings of the National Academy of Sciences, U.S.A.* 42: 855-863.

Myers, D. G. and E. Diener. 1995. "Who is Happy?" *Psychological Science* 6(1): 10-20.

Nelson, R. R. and S. G. Winter. 1982. *An Evolutionary Theory of Economic Change.* Cambridge, Mass.: Belknap Press of Harvard University Press.

Parker, G. A. 1970. "The Reproductive Behaviour and the Nature of Sexual Selection in *Scatophaga stercoria* L. (diptera: Scatophagiadae). II. The Fertilization Rate and the Spatial and Temporal Relationships of Each Sex Around the Site of Mating and Oviposition." *Journal of Animal Ecology* 39: 205-28.

Payne, R. B. 1977. "The Ecology of Brood Parasitism in Birds." *Annual Review of Ecology and Systematics* 8: 1-28.

Petrie, M. 1983. "Female Moorhens Compete for Small Fat Males." *Science* 220: 413-415.

Pinker, S. 1994. *The Language Instinct.* New York, NY: W. Morrow and Co.

Ricklefs, R. E. 1990. *Ecology.* Vol. W.H. Freeman. New York.

Robson, A. 1992. "Status, the Distribution of Wealth, Private and Social Attitudes Toward Risk." *Econometrica* 60(4): 837-58.

Robson, A. 1994a. "A Biological Basis for Expected and Non-Expected Utility."
University of Western Ontario working paper.

Robson, A. 1994b. "The Evolution of Attitudes to Risk: Lottery Tickets and Relative
Wealth." *Mimeo, University of Western Ontario.*

Rodseth, L., R. W. Wrangham, A. M. Harrigan and B. B. Smuts. 1991. "The Human
Community as a Primate Society." *Current Anthropology* 32(3): 221-254.

Rogers, A. R. 1994. "Evolution of Time Preference by Natural Selection." *American
Economic Review* 84(3): 460-481.

Rubin, P. H. and C. W. Paul. 1979. "An Evolutionary Model of Tastes for Risk."
Economic Inquiry 17(4): 585-96.

Ruvolo, M., D. Pan, S. Zehr, T. Goldberg, et al. 1994. "Gene Trees and Hominoid
Phylogeny." *Proceedings of the National Academy of Sciences of the U.S.A.* 91:
8900-8904.

Sahlins, M. D. 1972. *Stone Age Economics.* Chicago: Aldine-Atherton.

Samuelson, P. A. 1958. "An Exact Consumption-Loan Model of Interest With or Without
the Social Contrivance of Money." *Journal of Political Economy* 66(6): 467-482.

Samuelson, P. A. 1983. "Complete Genetic Models for Altruism, Kin Selection and Like-
Gene Selection." *Journal of Social and Biological Structures* 6(1): 3-15.

Samuelson, P. A. 1986. "Modes of Thought in Economics and Biology." in *The Collected Scientific papers of Paul A. Samuelson.* K. Crowley, Editor. Cambridge, Mass and London, England: The MIT Press. **V:** 723-729.

Samuelson, P. A. 1993. "Altruism as a Problem Involving Group versus Individual Selection in Economics and Biology." *American Economic Review* 83(2): 143-148.

Schelling, T. 1978. "Altruism, Meanness and Other Potentially Strategic Behaviors." *American Economic Review* 68(2): 229-30.

Sen, A. K. 1982. *Choice, Welfare, and Measurement.* Cambridge, Mass.: MIT Press.

Shepher, J. 1971. "Mate Selection among Second-Generation Kibbutz Adolescents and Adults: Incest Avoidance and Negative Imprinting." *Archives of Sexual Behavior* 1(4): 293-307.

Simon, H. 1993. "Altruism and Economics." *American Economic Review* 83(2): 156-161.

Stack, S. 1993. "The Effect of Modernization on Suicide in Finland: 1800-1984." *Sociological Perspectives* 36(2): 137-49.

Stanford, C. B. 1995. "Chimpanzee Hunting Behavior and Human Evolution." *American Scientist* 83(3): 256-62.

Tooby, J. and L. Cosmides. 1990. "The Past Explains the Present: Emotional Adaptations and the Structure of Ancestral Environments." *Ethology & Sociobiology* 11: 375-424.

Trivers, R. L. 1971. "The Evolution of Reciprocal Altruism." *Quarterly Review of Biology* 46(4): 35-57.

Tullock, G. 1978a. "Altruism, Malice, and Public Goods." *Journal of Social and Biological Structures* 1(1): 3-15.

Tullock, G. 1978b. "Altruism, Malice, and Public Goods: A Reply to Frech." *Journal of Social and Biological Structures* 1(2): 187-9.

Van Valen, L. 1973. "A New Evolutionary Law." *Evolutionary Theory* 1: 1-30.

Veenhoven, R. 1995. "World Database of Happiness." *Social Indicators Research* 34(3): 299-314.

Waldman. 1994. "Systematic Errors and the Theory of Natural Selection." *American Economic Review* 84(3): 482-497.

Williams, G. C. 1957. "Pleiotropy, Natural Selection, and the Evolution of Senescence." *Evolution* 11: 398-411.

Wilson, D. S. and E. Sober. 1994. "Group Selection: The Theory Replaces the Bogey Man." *Behavioral and Brain Sciences* 17(4): 639-655.

Wilson, E. O. 1975. *Sociobiology: The New Synthesis.* Cambridge, Mass.: Belknap Press
of Harvard University Press.

Wolf, A. P. 1995. *Sexual Attraction and Childhood Association: A Chinese Brief for
Edward Westermarck.* Stanford, Calif.: Stanford University Press.

Wrangham, R. W. 1987. "The Significance of African Apes for Reconstructing Human
Social Evolution." in *The Evolution of Human Behavior: Primate Models.* W. G.
Kinzey, Editor. Albany, N.Y.: State University of New York Press: 51-71.

Wrangham, R. W. 1993. "The Evolution of Sexuality in Chimpanzees and Bonobos."
Human Nature 4(1): 47-79.

Wynne-Edwards, V. C. 1986. *Evolution through Group Selection.* Oxford: Blackwell
Scientific Publications.

Yang, B. 1992. "The Economy and Suicide: A Time-Series Study of the U.S.A." *The
American Journal of Economics and Sociology* 51(1): 87-100.

Chapter 3: Genetic Evolution and Selfishness

Introduction

> How selfish soever man may be supposed, there are evidently some
> principles in his nature, which interest him in the fortune of others, and
> render their happiness necessary to him, though he derives nothing from it
> except the pleasure of seeing it.
> — Adam Smith
> *The Theory of Moral Sentiments, p. 9*

> Can we consider the sting of the wasp or of the bee as perfect, which, when
> used against many attacking animals, cannot be withdrawn, owing to the
> backward serratures, and so inevitably causes the death of the insect by
> tearing of its viscera?
> — Charles Darwin
> *On the Origin of Species, p. 202*

Economists and biologists have long grappled with the apparent contradiction of

altruism in a naturally selected world. Self-sacrifice and other voluntary acts that reduce

payoffs are unexpected if one assumes that evolution by natural selection favors

unmitigated self-interest. Nice people, it would seem, should finish last in evolutionary

competitions.

One means of reconciling evolution with an apparent lack of self-interest is to

place behavior in a larger, intertemporal context. Long-run self-interest may require a

variety of short-term sacrifices. This viewpoint has been expressed by a number of people

(Trivers, 1971; Schelling, 1978; Frank, 1988) and is formalized within economics in the

repeated game literature. Various theorems state that long-term maximizing strategies can

include almost any behavior in a particular period. Chapter 4 of this thesis examines one

such intertemporal strategy, that of reciprocal altruism.

This chapter also seeks to understand behavior in a larger context. Whereas the repeated game framework adds payoffs over time, this chapter looks across individuals at each moment in time. These two perspectives are conceptually orthogonal, but are simultaneously present in many situations.

In 1964, W.D. Hamilton (1964) energized behavioral biology by viewing "selfish genes" as the actual evolutionary competitors. Just as corporations are purported to act on behalf of their shareholders, Hamilton views individual organisms as doing the bidding for genetic owners. This chapter uses the selfish gene approach to analyze the incentives of individuals in two-person projects. Several papers have applied Hamilton's theory to other areas of economic behavior (Becker, 1976; Samuelson, 1983; Bergstrom and Stark, 1993; Samuelson, 1993; Bergstrom, 1995).

If genes expected to be equally represented in all individuals, they would be indifferent to the division of cooperative benefits. Continuing the shareholder analogy, a person who owns the same percentage of two companies does not care which receives the profit from joint efforts. Conflict between individuals exists because genes are not expected to be equally represented in all people. Thus, there is evolutionary pressure for behavior that varies based on the likelihood of shared genetic ownership.

Most economists do not explicitly link individual behavior to genes. However, the standard economic model does assume that all people share certain traits such as utility maximization. Insofar as this economic behavior is assumed to be inherently human it is implicitly genetic. This chapter makes the link explicit in the domain of selfishness by asking which behavioral genes are likely to survive.

A fundamental issue, two player cooperation and conflict

The "cooperation game"

      This chapter examines the situation below where one player decides the outcome for himself and for another player. The person in control can receive either C or 0 units of something that is desirable (money, for example). If the decider takes C then the other player receives D units, whereas if the decider takes 0 the other player also gets 0. The situation is a one time opportunity that will disappear forever after the payment of (C, D) or (0, 0).

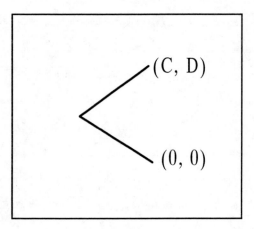

The cooperation game

      The payoff of (C, D) can be thought of as the difference in payoffs between joint and individual effort. If the players work individually, they receive payoffs that depend on feasibility and their own effort. Working together, player one receives the individual payoff plus an adjustment, C, which can be positive or negative. Similarly for player two and the adjustment, D.

Wanted, a method to predict conflict and shared interest

For any project (C, D) the attitude of the two players can, in principle, be determined. If the individuals are restricted to strictly preferring one of the two outcomes (not allowing indifference), then each value of (C, D) can be assigned to exactly one of the following four categories:

I: Shared interest to perform the project; both individuals prefer (C, D) to (0, 0).

II: Conflict of interest; player 1 prefers (C, D) to (0, 0) and player 2 prefers (0, 0) to (C, D).

III: Conflict of interest; player 1 prefers (0, 0) to (C, D) and player 2 prefers (C, D) to (0, 0).

IV: Shared interest to reject the project; both individuals prefer (0, 0) to (C, D).

Graphically, a theory of individual behavior divides the plane of payoffs into the four regions described above. In other words, for any particular C and D, a theory of behavior will have a prediction for the attitudes of both individuals towards the project.

D

A theory of individual
behavior divides the plane
into regions I, II, III, IV
which are disjoint and
include all values of (C, D)

C

Definition of a theory of individual behavior

Why this is an important issue

The cooperation game is important to an understanding of individual behavior, and it has relevance to a variety of larger issues. At the microeconomic level, this situation is the simplest involving interpersonal welfare issues. The situation is a one-time interaction and therefore all reputational issues are removed. Similarly, the payoffs are in a currency that is assumed to be unambiguously desirable. If a theory of individual behavior is to be applicable to complex situations, it would seem necessary to test the theory in a simple setting.

On a larger scale, the situation highlights issues of conflict, cooperation and societal well-being. For example, consider the implications if the payoffs represent net increases in wealth due to cooperation. The attitudes of the individuals in a society, combined with the available projects, will determine the wealth of that society. For example, suppose individuals undertake all projects where the sum of the payoffs is positive. A society composed of such individuals will achieve the highest feasible total wealth. Any other behavior will not result in societal wealth maximization.

Economic approach

Material self-interest

The neoclassical model of individual behavior states that individuals choose the best feasible alternative, where best means provides the most "utility". In the purely self-interested version of this model, people derive happiness and pleasure only from their own individual consumption. So, for example, a purely self-interested individual would watch his or her parents die with equanimity except for the impact on consumption through routes such as bequests.

The purely self-interest model makes a definite prediction about players in the cooperation game. For a purely self-interested player 1, the choice of (C, D) vs. (0, 0) reduces to the choice between C and 0. Assuming that the units to be distributed cause happiness (such as money) then player 1 prefers any positive C to 0. Similarly, player 2's attitude is determined solely by the sign of D.

Graphically, the pure-self interest model maps regions I, II, III and IV to entire quadrants of the payoff diagram as follows:

IV: <u>Conflict of interest</u> player 1 prefers (0, 0), player 2 preferes (C, D)	**I**: <u>Shared interest</u> Both players prefer (C, D) to (0, 0)
III: <u>Shared interest</u> Both players prefer (0, 0) to (C, D)	**II**: <u>Conflict of interest</u> player 1 prefers (C, D), player 2 preferes (0, 0)

The self-interested economic model's prediction of behavior

The data: Behavior at odds with economics' self-interested model

The self-interested economic model predicts that people will want to take all projects with positive individual payoff and want to avoid all projects with negative individual payoff. Human behavior significantly deviates from this economic model. Some of the most salient data are discussed below after the development of some behavioral terminology.

Altruism, spite, pride, and selflessness defined

Behavior that deviates from the self-interested economic model can be divided into four, distinct varieties. Choosing terminology for these behaviors presents a challenge. The words that seem most appropriate are often laden with multiple, contradictory meanings. After considerable reflection, the terms altruism, spite, pride and selflessness were chosen. The reader is advised to carefully review the following definitions and the accompanying diagram.

Altruism: Define altruism as a player being willing to undertake projects with negative personal payoff and positive payoff for the other player. For player 1 this means accepting projects with negative C and positive D.

Spite: Define spite as a player being willing to undertake projects with negative personal payoff and negative payoff for the other player. For player 1 this means accepting projects with negative C and negative D.

Pride: Define pride as a player being willing to reject projects with positive personal payoff and positive payoff for the other player. For player 1 this means rejecting projects with positive C and positive D.

Selflessness: Define selflessness as a player being willing to reject projects with positive personal payoff and negative payoff for the other player. For player 1 this means rejecting projects with positive C and negative D.

Altruism : Player 1 accepts a project with negative C and positive D	Pride : Player 1 rejects a project with positive C and positive D
Spite : Player 1 accepts a project with negative C and negative D	Selflessness : Player 1 rejects a project with positive C and negative D

Altruism, spite, pride, and selflessness defined

Laboratory data on non self-interested behavior

Altruism, spite, pride, and selflessness are cleanly demonstrated in a variety of laboratory experiments. The next two sections review some of the best evidence of behavior at odds with the economic model of self-interest.

Pride in ultimatum games

Perhaps the most famous economic experiment is the so-called ultimatum game, first performed experimentally in 1982 (Guth et al., 1982). The simplest ultimatum game is structured as follows. One person, called the proposer, divides an amount of money into two parts. This division is presented to a second person, termed the responder, as a take it or leave it offer (hence the name ultimatum). The responder can accept the proposed division or reject the ultimatum. In both cases the game ends with the responder's decision. If the responder rejects, then both parties receive nothing.

The responder faces exactly the cooperation game as defined in the beginning of this chapter:

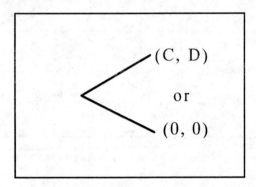

The decision faced by ultimatum game responders

A robust finding in ultimatum games is that responders exhibit pride, as defined in this chapter. Specifically, when responders are offered small portions of the financial pie, they choose (0, 0) over (C, D) even when they would receive substantial amounts. Guth, Schmittberger, and Schwarze report overall rejection rates of more than 10%. The findings were originally disputed by economists, but they have been extensively replicated and are now broadly accepted. (See chapter 4 of Kagel and Roth, 1995 for a review.)

Altruism in dictator games

The dictator game has the same structure as the ultimatum game except the second player does not have the right to refuse the division. Player 1's decision is unilaterally imposed (thus the name dictator). Because of this change, player 2 is called the recipient in dictator games, as opposed to the responder in ultimatum games. Three published studies

(Forsythe et al., 1994; Hoffman et al., 1994; Hoffman et al., 1996) report substantial and persistent altruism, again as defined in this chapter, in dictator games.

The dictator can take all the money for himself. Consider a dictator who gives one dollar to the recipient and keeps nine dollars. In the language of this chapter, this dictator has voluntarily chosen a project with a C of -1 and a D of +1. This is precisely the definition of altruism.

These three studies and the results in chapter 4 of this thesis show that the level of altruism in dictator games is systematically altered by the context. In Hoffman, McCabe, and Smith (1996) five treatments are studied which vary the privacy of the dictator. In the most private version, approximately one-third of dictators exhibit altruism as compared to more than eighty percent in the most public version. In all the studies, however, altruism persists at significant levels.

Non self-interested behavior outside the laboratory

Daily life is filled with behavior that appears to conform to this chapter's definition of altruism, spite, pride and selflessness. Whereas the laboratory controls all factors except one or two, outside the lab there are always additional factors. The hard-hearted can find solace in these factors and cling to a notion of narrow self-interest.

A person picking up litter on a deserted night time street would, for example, appear to be acting altruistically. A cynic, however, can argue that there is always some chance of discovery, and this seemingly altruistic act is an attempt to garner societal rewards. A similar argument can be made for all behavior that appears to deviate from self-interest including blood donations, other acts of charity (even anonymous), violence,

86

and strikes. The attempt to *prove* that people are not narrowly self-interested is doomed

to failure. The direct explanation for the behaviors discussed in the next several sections

is, however, evidence for a richer model of human behavior.

The voter paradox

The fact that millions of people vote in elections is known as the voter paradox.

The reason it is considered a paradox is as follows. The act of voting is costly because it

takes time and effort. The effect of any single vote on the outcome in a modern election is

zero. For example, the margin of victory in 20th century U.S. Presidential elections ranges

from thousands to more than ten million.

The act of voting presumably confers some benefit on others. If no one voted then

the outcome would be worse than the current outcome, or so the argument goes. In the

notation of this chapter, voting is act where C, the payoff to the voter, is negative, but D,

the payoff to society, is positive. The act of voting then is classified in this chapter's

scheme as altruism.

Violence between strangers

A study (Cohen et al., 1996) of the causes of U.S. violence states: "Approximately

20,000 - 25,000 Americans will die in homicides this year, and tens of thousand more will

be injured in stabbings or gunfights that could have ended in death." Among the deadly

disputes that take place between strangers, a theme emerges. Some slight occurs

(highways and bars are common locations) and a fight ensues that leads to death or

serious injury. In the notation of this chapter, these fights are acts with costs to both parties. The willingness to participate in such a fight, is, again in the lexicon of this chapter, an act of spite.

Summary thoughts on narrow self-interest

Daily life, experimental data and common sense indicate that a model of human behavior based only on individual, material self-interest can only be valid in a tautological sense.

Economic attempts to incorporate altruism, spite, pride, and selflessness

The formal attempts by economists to build a richer model of behavior are discussed in detail in chapter 4 of this thesis. Many serious, talented individuals have attempted to build models consistent with behavior as exhibited in the laboratory and beyond. The outcome to date can, at best, be described as hopeful beginnings: The models that are consistent with data have little predictive power, whereas those with predictive power are inconsistent with the data.

The promise of genetic evolutionary theory

The "problem of altruism" is a debate over human nature. Economic models start by making a variety of assumptions about human desires and the means for attaining those desires. In particular, most economic theory is built upon an assumption that people are entirely selfish.

As discussed above, people are not entirely selfish. Economics has not been able to satisfactorily understand and incorporate non-selfish behavior. Furthermore, human nature with regard to interpersonal concerns is an assumption of economics and thus economic theory can provide absolutely no help in resolving this issue. As discussed in Chapter 2 of this thesis, the debate of about selfishness is precisely the sort of problem where genetic evolutionary theory is likely to help.

The basic message of evolutionary theory is genes that replicate themselves most successfully are the ones that survived and exist. Behavioral biology is built on this theory and is implemented as follows. In any given situation, first write down the reproductive payoffs to the feasible behavior. Second, analytically solve for the behavior that maximizes reproductive success. The final step is a prediction about behavior; organisms are predicted to act as if they are seeking to maximize their reproductive success.

Contrast the evolutionary and the standard economic approaches. Are people selfish? In economics, the approach has been to assume yes and test the assumption. The empirical conclusion is that people combine self-interest with selflessness in a manner that has eluded succinct economic description. Accordingly, the standard models in economics assume complete selfishness.

Now bring in the tools of genetic evolutionary theory and again ask if people are selfish. Genetic evolutionary theory allows the attitudes to be **derived** from more fundamental assumptions. Specifically, the model that is developed below, asks what form of interpersonal preferences would be favored to evolve by natural selection.

Inclusive fitness theory

The original Darwinian view was that successful replication requires survival and children. In 1964, W.D. Hamilton (Hamilton, 1964) proposed that Darwin's theory should be modified to view genes, not individuals, as the relevant evolutionary competitors. This theory, known as either *inclusive fitness theory* or *kin selection*, allowed a major advance in behavioral biology.

Prior to Hamilton, a variety of behaviors, including some forms of altruism, seemed to contradict basic Darwinian theory. Inclusive fitness theory resolved many of these apparent paradoxes, and fostered an integrated study of the genetic roots of behavior. Because it is central to the model in this chapter, the next sections discuss inclusive theory in some detail before employing the concept.

Hamilton's theory has been much debated and studied (see (Michod, 1982), for a review). The particulars of when Hamilton's rule can be used exactly as assumed below have been modified, but the essential insight is accepted by mainstream natural scientists.

Kin-biased behavior

A basic insight of Hamilton is that genes are more likely to be shared among relatives than non-relatives. The relevant probability of sharing genes, *the coefficient of relatedness*, is defined below, but individuals share more genetic material with closer relatives than with more distant relatives. One consequence is that evolution will select genes that encode for certain kin-biased behavior.

Hamilton's rule

Operationally, kin selection theory works via "Hamilton's rule" which totals the effect of an action across all individuals. The *direct fitness* of an action for an individual is defined as the change in the number of surviving, fertile offspring caused by the action. The *inclusive fitness* of an individual is defined as the direct fitness plus the effect on shared genes in other individuals derived from recent common ancestors.

90

Consider individual i, in a population of size N, who has the option of performing a certain action. Denote the <u>direct</u> fitness consequences of the action on individual j as f_j.

Define r_{ij} as the *coefficient of relatedness* between individual i and j. r_{ij} is the likelihood that individual j shares a particular genetic sequence with individual i from recent common ancestors. Hamilton's rule calculates individual i's <u>inclusive</u> fitness from the action as $f_i + \sum\limits_{\substack{j=1,N \\ j \neq i}} r_{ij} f_j$. The inclusive fitness of an act for an individual is the direct fitness impact on that individual plus the effect on other individuals weighted by the likelihood of shared genetic material.

Coefficient of relatedness

The coefficient of relatedness, r, is a probability that two individuals share a particular genetic sequence from recent common ancestors. Because r is a probability it can take values from 0 to 1 inclusively. Unrelated individuals have a coefficient equal to 0, and identical twins have a coefficient equal to 1.

Given a family lineage, r can be calculated. Humans have two copies of every gene, but only pass one along to each offspring. The chance of a gene variant being transmitted between generations is therefore one-half. For each path linking two individuals the contribution to r is $\dfrac{1}{2^S}$ where S is the number of generations separating the two people. If there are multiple common ancestors, then the contribution for each ancestor is calculated separately and added together. Some important examples are, offspring and parents with r = 0.5, full siblings with r = 0.5, grandchildren and grandparents with r = 0.25.

A genetic evolutionary economic model

Introduction

The model applies inclusive fitness theory to bilateral cooperation. This is done by calculating the inclusive fitness effects of the cooperation game described at the beginning of this chapter. The goal is to characterize the set of projects that individuals prefer to the status quo.

The solution concept is maximal relative growth rate. Evolution selects for entities that increase as a percentage of the population. As stated above, the prediction is straightforward; entities that exist today replicated at higher rates than their competitors.

The model is very simple. This is justified because it is the first model of its type within the economics literature. The simple question has never been addressed within economics and it is: What type of interpersonal preferences would be favored by natural selection?

Model Setup

- N, Population (≥ 2)

- players are individuals denoted as 1, 2, ... , N

- define r_{ij} as the coefficient of relatedness between players i and j

- Consider a project that yields C direct fitness units to individual 1 and D direct fitness units to individual 2.

<u>Goal:</u> Characterize the sets of projects, described by values of C and D, that players 1 and 2 would like to undertake.

<u>Solution Method:</u> Calculate the inclusive fitness payoffs to each player. Assume each player acts, whenever feasible, to maximize inclusive fitness.

$\alpha \equiv$ the inclusive fitness effect of project (C, D) on player 1. α a function of C, D, N, and r_{ij}'s

$\beta \equiv$ the inclusive fitness effect of project (C, D) on player 2. β a function of C, D, N, and r_{ij}'s.

A theory of behavior was defined earlier in this chapter as mapping all possible (C, D) into one of four regions. Genetic evolutionary theory predicts that player 1 will want to undertake projects where $\alpha > 0$, and player 2 will want to undertake projects where $\beta > 0$.

Consider a particular project that increases the inclusive fitness of both players. This means that when the particulars of N and the r_{ij}'s are combined with the project payoffs according to the formula derived below, both α and β are both greater than zero. The genetic evolutionary prediction is that both players will prefer this project to the status quo. Using the definitions from earlier in this chapter, such a project is placed in region I where players share an interest to perform the project.

Alternatively, consider a project that results in positive α and negative β. Genetic evolutionary theory predicts player 1 will want to undertake this project and player 2 will

93

prefer the status quo. Using the definitions from earlier in this chapter, such a project is placed in region II where the players have a conflict of interest over the project.

The following diagram summarizes the prediction about both players' attitudes towards a project as a function of the project's inclusive fitness consequences.

		Effect of project (C, D) on player 1's inclusive fitness	
		decrease	increase
Effect of project (C, D) on player 2's inclusive fitness	increase	IV: <u>Conflict of interest</u> player 1 prefers (0, 0), player 2 prefers (C, D)	I: <u>Shared interest</u> Both players prefer (C, D) to (0, 0)
	decrease	III: <u>Shared interest</u> Both players prefer (0, 0) to (C, D)	II: <u>Conflict of interest</u> player 1 prefers (C, D), player 2 prefers (0, 0)

Inclusive fitness predictions for behavior.

Zero-sum nature of genetic conflict

In the solution below, the overall population is assumed to remain constant. Thus, if players 1 and 2 undertake a project with payoffs of (C, D), the population, as a whole, must have an offsetting adjustment of -(C+D). This adjustment is assumed to be spread evenly over all members of the population, including players 1 and 2. Thus, if the project is undertaken every member of the population receives an adjustment of $-\dfrac{(C+D)}{N}$.

The appendix to this chapter demonstrates that the constant population formulation is equivalent to characterizing the behaviors that increase as a percentage of a variable sized population. In other words, the method used in the body of this chapter is equivalent to the standard evolutionary prediction of selecting behaviors with the highest relative replication rates.

With a <u>variable</u> population size the payoffs in **direct** fitness units if project (C, D) is performed are:

Player 1:	+C
Player 2:	+D
Players 3 through N:	0

If the variable population approach is used, absolute values need to be converted into growth rates as shown in the appendix. If the population is assumed fixed, the direct payoffs are modified, but no calculation of growth rates is required.

The rest of this chapter uses the second approach with following altered payoffs in **direct** fitness units if project (C, D) is performed:

Player 1: $+C - \dfrac{(C + D)}{N}$

Player 2: $+D - \dfrac{(C + D)}{N}$

Players 3 through N: $-\dfrac{(C + D)}{N}$ per individual

General form of solution

Calculate payoffs in **inclusive** fitness units by applying Hamilton's rule

$\alpha =$ player 1's direct fitness payoff + r_{12} * player 2's direct fitness payoff

$+ \displaystyle\sum_{k=3}^{N} r_{1k}$ * player k's direct fitness payoffs for k = [3, N]

$\beta =$ player 2's direct fitness payoff + r_{21} * player 1's direct fitness payoff

$+ \displaystyle\sum_{k=3}^{N} r_{2k}$ * player k's direct fitness payoffs for k = [3, N]

$$\alpha = +C - \frac{(C + D)}{N} + r_{12}\left(+D - \frac{(C + D)}{N}\right) + \sum_{k=3}^{N} r_{1k}\frac{-(C + D)}{N}$$

$$\alpha = C\left(1 - \frac{1 + r_{12} + \displaystyle\sum_{k=3}^{N} r_{1k}}{N}\right) + D\left(r_{12} - \frac{1 + r_{12} + \displaystyle\sum_{k=3}^{N} r_{1k}}{N}\right)$$

define $r_{1Avg} = \dfrac{1 + r_{12} + \sum\limits_{k=3}^{N} r_{1k}}{N}$, the average coefficient of relationship between player 1

and all N members of population (including player 1.)

$\Rightarrow$ $$\boxed{\alpha = C\left(1 - r_{1Avg}\right) + D\left(r_{12} - r_{1Avg}\right)}$$

Similarly,

$$\boxed{\beta = C\left(r_{21} - r_{2Avg}\right) + D\left(1 - r_{2Avg}\right)}$$

where $r_{2Avg} = \dfrac{1 + r_{21} + \sum\limits_{k=3}^{N} r_{2k}}{N}$

Analysis: Behavior as a function of kinship

Examine projects from player 1's perspective: $\alpha = C\left(1 - r_{1Avg}\right) + D\left(r_{12} - r_{1Avg}\right)$

- Examine the coefficient for C, $1 - r_{1Avg}$. By definition all r's are between 0 (non-

  relative) and 1 (identical twin) inclusively. As long as the population has at least one

  individual who is not a genetic clone of player 1, r_{1Avg} is strictly less than 1 and α is

  strictly increasing in C.

- Examine the coefficient for D, $r_{12} - r_{1Avg}$. The only constraint is that $0 \le r_{12} \le 1$ so

  α can be increasing or decreasing in D.

$\Rightarrow$ The model predicts that player 1's inclusive fitness increases in C, but may increase or

decrease in D.

Dealing with close relatives

If $r_{12} > r_{1Avg}$ then player 1 is closer to player 2 than to the overall population,

and the inclusive fitness of player 1 increases with increases in D. In this case, genetic

evolutionary theory predicts that player 1 will exhibit altruism and selflessness towards

player 2, within limits. These limits are of two types. First, player 1 will accept some

costs to bestow benefits upon player 2. Altruism and selflessness, even towards close kin,

is bounded.

Second, player 1 is concerned for player 2 only by force of circumstances. Given a

choice, player 1 would always prefer to receive the benefits of an action directly. In other

words, player 1 always prefers (C+D, 0) to (C, D). A final point is that being a relative (r

> 0) is not enough to obtain favors. Kin-based benefits are bestowed upon those with

relatedness above the average for the population as shown:

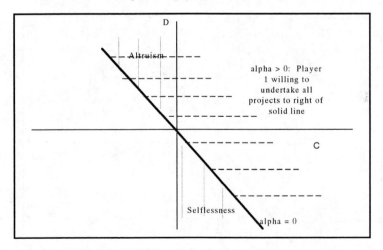

Altruism and selflessness towards close kin, $r_{12} > r_{1AVG}$

Dealing with people other than close relatives

> A goddess visited a farmer and promised to grant one wish with an
> interesting twist. The farmer would be granted his wish, but each of his
> neighbors would receive the wish in duplicate. After a moment's reflection
> the farmer asked that half his crops be destroyed.
> — Ukrainian folk tale

If $r_{12} < r_{1Avg}$ then player 1 is closer to the average for the overall population than to

player 2. In this case, the inclusive fitness of player 1 decreases with increases in D.

Genetic evolutionary theory predicts that player 1 will exhibit spite and pride in dealing

with everyone other than close kin. Two caveats similar to those in the altruism and

selflessness discussion are appropriate. First, players are predicted to accept limited costs

to damage others. Second, player 1 would always prefer to reduce both parties' costs by

equal amounts. In other words $(C + x, D + x)$ where x is positive, is always preferred to

(C, D). The case of dealing with people other than close kin is summarized below:

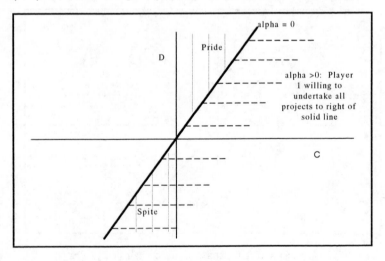

Pride and spite towards close non-close kin, $r_{12} < r_{1AVG}$

99

Evolutionarily world

A simplified view of the environment in which humans evolved is small groups of related individuals. A group might consist of, at most, a few hundred individuals all related to each other with a coefficient of relatedness greater than zero. People from one group would periodically interact with neighboring individuals. A person might therefore productively classify all other people into one of three groups: close kin, distant kin, and stranger. Close kin being siblings, parents, grandparents, and perhaps some cousins and other distant relatives. Everyone within the group who was not close kin could be assumed to be distant kin. Individuals from other groups would be likely to have much lower shared genetic component, and would be classified as strangers.

The analysis above indicates that evolution would favor different behaviors towards these three types of people. Close kin would be treated the best, and strangers the worst. In all cases, the individual cares more about his or her own payoff than about the payoffs for others.

Combine players 1 and 2

The effects of kinship on player 2's incentives are analyzed in the same fashion as for player 1. Specifically, the model predicts that player 2's inclusive fitness increases in D, but may increase or decrease in C. Human coefficients of relatedness are symmetric so $r_{12} = r_{21}$. There are three possible cases. Two are shown in the following diagrams and the third case (where $r_{2Avg} > r_{21} = r_{12} > r_{1Avg}$) is a straightforward extrapolation.

A conclusion is that all human relationships have regions of conflict and shared interest. The effect of increasing kinship is to increase the zone of shared interest. In this light conflict and cooperation are equally "natural", and the resulting behavior will depend on the circumstances.

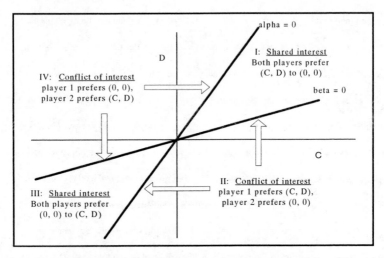

Behavioral predictions for interactions between non-close kin.

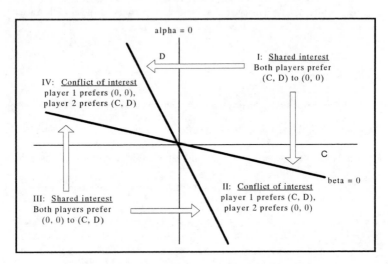

Behavioral predictions for interactions between close kin.

Analysis: Behavior as a function of population size, N

Consider a particular case as follows:

Player #	expected coefficient of relatedness with player 1
1	1
2	r_{12}
3-> P+2	r_{1k} **(P relatives of player 1)**
P+3-> N	r_{12} with $r_{1k} > r_{12}$ $\forall k \in [3, P+2]$

From the perspective of player 1 the world divides into three groups: self, direct

relatives, and others. This can be considered the standard case when a person interacts

with someone they know is not a direct relative, but about whom they have no additional

kin information. The general solution derived above is still applicable. The inclusive

fitness for player 1 is α where $\alpha = C\left(1 - r_{1Avg}\right) + D\left(r_{12} - r_{1Avg}\right)$

and $r_{1Avg} = \dfrac{1 + r_{12} + \sum\limits_{k=3}^{N} r_{1k}}{N}$ which in this case simplifies to

$$r_{1Avg} = \frac{1 + r_{12} + \sum\limits_{k=3}^{P+2} r_{1k} + \sum\limits_{m=P+3}^{N} r_{12}}{N} = \frac{1 + \sum\limits_{k=3}^{P+2} r_{1k} + (N - P - 1)r_{12}}{N}$$

Two observations can be made. First, player 2 can never be close kin as defined

by sharing more genetic material with player 1 than the average for the entire population

(r_{12} is strictly less than r_{1Avg}). The point is that a person is related less to an "average"

non-relative then to the overall average, which includes direct relatives. This argues that

the standard, day-to-day interaction with people is one that triggers the spite and pride.

Second, the behavior can be parameterized as a function of total population, N. In

this case $\boxed{\lim_{N \to \infty} r_{1Avg} = r_{12}} \Rightarrow \boxed{\lim_{N \to \infty} \alpha = kC}$ where k is a positive constant. As N

increases, the zone of cooperation increases. At the limit, the genetic model approaches

the neo-classical purely self-interested model as shown in the following diagram.

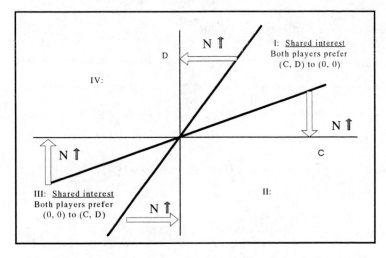

Interactions with non direct kin as a function of population size, N

Discussion

Human brains "assume" small population sizes

The first message of this model is that optimal behavior depends on the population size. In particular, in small populations every action has a strategic component. Evolution is a relative game and competition and cooperation walk side by side. Participation in a project with unequal rewards may create a powerful rivals. Equally dangerous, from an evolutionary point of view, is the failure to work together when there are gains from cooperation.

An explanation for a variety of modern behaviors lies in the much smaller population sizes (N in the model above) that have been the human historical norm. To the extent that the historically small N has been fixed in our behavioral patterns, humans will inappropriately act as strategists in some modern situations. This is one explanation for the voter paradox described earlier in this chapter. Our behavioral patterns "assume" that we live in a small community where input into a group decision is likely to influence the outcome. A similar logic applies to a variety of behaviors where individuals are infinitesimal players in modern settings, but historically had influential roles.

Increasing shared interest through kinship

Kinship plays a major role in determining the amount of shared interest. As the players become closer relatives, the regions of shared interest (I and III) increase in size while those with a conflict of interest (II and IV) shrink. At an extreme, when the coefficient of relatedness equals 1, the two parties have identical interests and the zones of conflict disappear.

At first glance this result may appear unimportant to human nature. Only identical twins have no genetic conflict, and they are rare. Look inside a human body and the importance of kinship will be clear. All the individual cells in a multicellular organism share the same genes. We find it surprising when a person gives his or her life for another person, but we do not find it strange when an immune system cell dies for its siblings. Both behaviors result from the same evolutionary forces with a different level of kinship.

A second human phenomenon is also caused by the effect of kinship on the amount of genetic conflict. In all human societies, individuals tend to live with, and interact most frequently with, their genetic kin. This kin-biased interaction is a method to increase the amount of shared interest.

Shaping the available projects to minimize conflict

The model predicts behavior as a function of the project payoffs, C and D, but it does not address the sources of the available projects. In other words, the set of available projects is taken as fixed. Individuals, however, may have the ability to alter the set of available projects. In particular, a very common alteration might be to move projects from zones of conflict to zones of shared interest.

Consider, for example, the "violence project" which involves a large individual (the "aggressor") hurting a smaller individual (the "victim") who is not a close relative. Suppose, for argument's sake, that the smaller individual cannot significantly hurt the larger individual in a fight. In this case, the violence project will increase the aggressor's inclusive fitness and decrease the victim's inclusive fitness.

The genetic evolutionary prediction is that violence projects of this form will be performed. The aggressor and the victim have a conflict of interest over the violence project, but the aggressor, by assumption, has the power to implement the project over the objections of the victim. The following diagram places the violence in region II of the behavioral mapping.

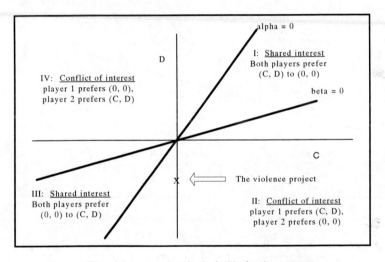

The violence project is desirable for the aggressor

The prediction is that, under these circumstances, natural selection would favor large humans who kill or harm smaller non-relatives even without any material gain. Do we see such behavior? No, such behavior is uncommon for humans, even in societies without police or other governmental sanction.

One reason that we see so few of these sorts of behaviors is that the projects do not exist. Consider a second project, called the "blood revenge project". This is the action by genetic relatives of the victim upon the aggressor. Such a behavior is likely to have costs to both the aggressor and the relatives of the victim. Consider the combined payoff to violence and revenge as shown next:

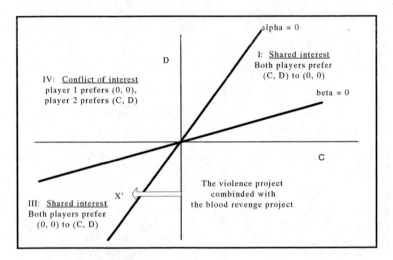

Violence with revenge is not desirable for the aggressor.

Blood revenge is a human universal and it serves to modify the available projects. As shown, the revenge must be sufficiently severe to move the net payoffs into a region of shared interest.

Concluding comments

> ...our genes have survived, in some cases for millions of years, in a highly competitive world. This entitles us to expect certain qualities in our genes. I shall argue that a predominant quality to be expected in a successful gene is ruthless selfishness.
>
> — Richard Dawkins
> *The Selfish Gene*, p. 2

Several of the apparent paradoxes in individual behavior are caused by an incorrect assumption that evolution favors selfish individuals. The actual evolutionary competitors are genes who pursue their goals through individuals. There is no general rule as to the type of behavior at the organism level-- cooperation is as likely as conflict, and depends on the circumstances.

Literature cited

Becker, G. 1976. "Altruism, Egoism, and Genetic Fitness: Economics and Sociobiology." *Journal of Economic Literature* XIV(3): 817-826.

Bergstrom, T. 1995. "On the Evolution of Altruistic Ethical Rules for Siblings." *American Economic Review* 85(1): 58-81.

Bergstrom, T. and O. Stark. 1993. "How Altruism can Prevail in an Evolutionary Environment." *American Economic Review* 83(2): 149-155.

Cohen, D., R. E. Nisbett, B. F. Bowdle and N. Schwarz. 1996. "Insult, Aggression, and the Southern Culture of Honor: An 'Experimental Ethnography'." *Journal of Personality & Social Psychology* 70: 945-960.

Forsythe, R., J. L. Horowitz, N. E. Savin and M. Sefton. 1994. "Fairness in Simple Bargaining Experiments." *Games and Economic Behavior* 6(3): 347-69.

Frank, R. H. 1988. *Passions Within Reason.* New York: W. W. Norton & Company.

Guth, W., R. Schmittberger and B. Schwarze. 1982. "An Experimental Analysis of Ultimatum Bargaining." *Journal of Economic Behavior and Organization* 3: 367-388.

Hamilton, W. D. 1964. "The Genetical Evolution of Social Behavior I and II." *Journal of Theoretical Biology* 7: 1-16, 17-52.

Hoffman, E., K. McCabe, K. Shachat and V. Smith. 1994. "Preferences, Property Rights, and Anonymity in Bargaining Games." *Games and Economic Behavior* 7: 346-380.

Hoffman, E., K. McCabe and V. L. Smith. 1996. "Social Distance and Other-Regarding Behavior in Dictator Games." *American Economic Review* 86(3): 653.

Kagel, J. H. and A. E. Roth, Editors. 1995. *The Handbook of Experimental Economics.* Princeton, N.J.: Princeton University Press.

Michod, R. E. 1982. "The Theory of Kin Selection." *Annual Review of Ecology and Systematics* 13:: 23-55.

Samuelson, P. A. 1983. "Complete Genetic Models for Altruism, Kin Selection and Like-Gene Selection." *Journal of Social and Biological Structures* 6(1): 3-15.

Samuelson, P. A. 1993. "Altruism as a Problem Involving Group versus Individual Selection in Economics and Biology." *American Economic Review* 83(2): 143-148.

Schelling, T. 1978. "Altruism, Meanness and Other Potentially Strategic Behaviors." *American Economic Review* 68(2): 229-30.

Trivers, R. L. 1971. "The Evolution of Reciprocal Altruism." *Quarterly Review of Biology* 46(4): 35-57.

<u>Appendix - Relative growth rates</u>

This appendix shows that the fixed population assumption used in the main part of the chapter is identical to analyzing the effect of a project on relative genetic growth rates. The relative growth rate approach may appear more satisfactory because it simply states that existing genes out replicated their competitors. The discussion in this chapter assumes that any gains from cooperation must be offset by losses somewhere. Even when the population is not fixed, the competition at the genetic level is zero-sum. Competing gene variants are fighting for percentages of a particular chromosomal location. Any gain in one variant's percentage must come from other variants.

Case 1: All copies of gene from recent common ancestor

Number of copies without project: $1 + r_{12} + \sum\limits_{k=3}^{N} r_{1k}$

Number of copies with project: $1 + r_{12} + \sum\limits_{k=3}^{N} r_{1k} + C + Dr_{12}$

Percentage without project $= \dfrac{1 + r_{12} + \sum\limits_{k=3}^{N} r_{1k}}{N}$

Percentage with project $= \dfrac{1 + r_{12} + \sum\limits_{k=3}^{N} r_{1k} + C + Dr_{12}}{N + C + D}$

$\Rightarrow$ gene is increasing as a percentage of population if $\dfrac{C + Dr_{12}}{C + D} > \dfrac{1 + r_{12} + \sum\limits_{k=3}^{N} r_{1k}}{N}$

111

$\Leftrightarrow$ increasing if $(C + Dr_{12})N > (C + D)\left(1 + r_{12} + \sum\limits_{k=3}^{N} r_{1k}\right)$

$$\Leftrightarrow (C + Dr_{12}) - (C + D)\dfrac{\left(1 + r_{12} + \sum\limits_{k=3}^{N} r_{1k}\right)}{N} > 0$$

$$\boxed{C\left(1 - r_{1Avg}\right) + D\left(r_{12} - r_{1Avg}\right) > 0}$$

where $r_{1avg} = \dfrac{1 + r_{12} + \sum\limits_{k=3}^{N} r_{1k}}{N}$, identical to result in main part of this chapter.

Case 2: gene has percentage p of locations not from recent common ancestor

Among genes not from recent common ancestor assume p percent are shared

Total population = N

Copies of gene of interest from recent common ancestor =

$$1 + r_{12} + \sum\limits_{k=3}^{N} r_{1k} = N\left(\dfrac{1 + r_{12} + \sum\limits_{k=3}^{N} r_{1k}}{N}\right) = Nr_{1Avg}$$

Copies of gene existing, but not from recent ancestor =

$$p(1 - r_{12}) + p\sum\limits_{k=3}^{N}(1 - r_{1k}) = p\left(N - 1 - r_{12} - \sum\limits_{k=3}^{N} r_{1k}\right)$$

$$= \frac{pN\left(N - 1 - r_{12} - \sum_{k=3}^{N} r_{1k}\right)}{N} = pN\left(\frac{N}{N} - \frac{1 - r_{12} - \sum_{k=3}^{N} r_{1k}}{N}\right)$$

$$= pN\left(1 - r_{1Avg}\right)$$

Total copies for gene of interest $= Nr_{1Avg} + Np\left(1 - r_{1Avg}\right)$

gene's percentage of population without project $= r_{1Avg} + p\left(1 - r_{1Avg}\right)$

increase due to project $= C + D$

increase in gene of interest $= C + r_{12}D + p\left(1 - r_{12}\right)D$

gene of interest's share of increase $= \dfrac{C + r_{12}D + p\left(1 - r_{12}\right)D}{C + D}$

gene of interest will grow as a percentage of population if gene's share of project exceeds gene's existing share. Compare share of increase with share of existing population.

$$\frac{C + r_{12}D + p\left(1 - r_{12}\right)D}{C + D} > ?\ r_{1Avg} + p\left(1 - r_{1Avg}\right)$$

Simplify:

$$C\left(1 - r_{1Avg} - p + pr_{1Avg}\right) + D\left(r_{12} + p - pr_{12} - r_{1Avg} - p + pr_{1Avg}\right)$$

$$= \boxed{C\left(1 - p\right)\left(1 - r_{1Avg}\right) + D\left(1 - p\right)\left(r_{12} - r_{1Avg}\right)}$$ for all p < 1, this result is identical to the

result in body of the chapter.

Chapter 4: Engineering Altruism

Introduction

A standard assumption in many parts of economics is that individuals pursue material self-interest without regard for others. Experimental evidence that contradicts this narrow self-interest has accumulated in the years since Guth, Schmittberger, and Schwarze (1982) first performed experiments on ultimatum games. At least two deviations from narrow self-interest have been firmly established. (See ch. 3 of this thesis, ch. 4 in Kagel and Roth, 1995 and Guth, 1995 for summaries.)

First, experimental subjects willingly take lower payoffs to avoid situations that can be described as "unfair". The most famous of these situations is the refusal of ultimatum game recipients to accept unequal splits. Second, subjects often are willing to take lower payoffs in order to *increase* another person's payout. This has been shown in a variety of settings including public goods (Andreoni, 1995) and dictator games where a significant percentage of subjects give money to their recipients. (Forsythe et al., 1994; Hoffman et al., 1994; Hoffman et al., 1996)

These results, if representative of non-laboratory behavior, have considerable importance for economics. A number of theorists (Bolton, 1991; Rabin, 1993; Levine, 1995) have proposed preference structures that are more consistent with experimental evidence than the narrow self-interest model. These models share the perspective that experimental results are the outcome of subjects maximizing stable preferences, and not caused by irrationality.

114

Because the term altruism is used with many meanings, a definition is in order. In this chapter, altruism is defined as a **voluntary** action that **materially** hurts the actor and materially benefits some other entity. This definition encompasses charitable acts such as donating to the Red Cross as well as giving gifts without an explicit promise of repayment.

Along with economists, biologists have long been interested in the question of altruism. The leading view in natural science is that gifts to non-relatives have selfish origins. Put forth by Robert Trivers (1971) under the title "reciprocal altruism," this view holds that mutual advantage can be gained by alternating roles of giver and receiver.

Two subtleties of reciprocal altruism merit note. First, the theory does not require that every gift be repaid. It is sufficient that the average amount returned, in units of reproductive success, be greater than the gift. Second, in non-equilibrium situations, even this condition may not be met. The second point is of particular relevance as there is good reason to believe human genes are not in equilibrium with industrial conditions.

Population size and group dynamics are of particular relevance to the study of gift giving. Until relatively recently, on an evolutionary time scale, humans lived in small groups (Tooby and Cosmides, 1990). In this setting, all interpersonal relationships involve frequent, repeated interactions. Gift giving behavior that is appropriate for this repeated framework, may appear puzzling in novel situations such as one-shot games -- whether in the laboratory or on the street.

This chapter merges the economic and biological views on altruism. More precisely, it builds an economic model on a natural science foundation. A simple reciprocal altruism model is developed in the form of a two person, exchange economy. The model produces a set of predictions with regard to altruism. A plethora of potentially confusing surface phenomena mask the underlying unity of reciprocal altruism theory. Naturally selected organisms sometimes behave like altruists, because altruism pays, or at least paid during the period in which the behavior arose.

One of the robust findings of experimental economics and psychology is that behavior is powerfully influenced by factors outside of traditional economic analysis. In particular, while economics largely focuses on the formal structure, other research, for example (Kahneman and Tversky, 1984; Hoffman et al., 1994; Hoffman et al., 1996), has shown the importance of context, or "framing". To date, the debate has largely centered on the existence, robustness, and relevance of frames. This chapter attempts to address the origin of frames, and in particular seeks their genesis in evolution by natural selection.

In search of Darwinian origins, the reciprocal altruism model motivates the experiments contained. One of the model's predictions is that gift giving will be very sensitive to the likelihood of future interaction. Furthermore, the genetic evolutionary model predicts that frames can be engineered based on modern or ancient environmental cues. The experiment is designed to induce altruism through one modern and one ancient factor.

The rest of this chapter is structured as follows. The first section reminds the reader of the role of self-interest in several areas of economics. While any form of interpersonal preferences is technically valid, standard proofs of important results rely upon narrow self-interest. The second section recounts evidence that narrow self-interest is not a complete description of human behavior. (See chapter 3 of this thesis for more discussion on behavior and material self-interest.)

116

The third section discusses formal models of preferences that are more consistent with the experimental data. There has been a fruitful empirical-theoretic cycle in this area. Experiments motivated new models which in turn motivated more experiments and new theories. The fourth section presents the evolutionary model of reciprocal altruism and its predictions for gift giving. The experimental design and results follow. The chapter concludes with a brief discussion of the experimental results in a broader context.

The role of self-interest in economic theory

> How selfish soever man may be supposed, there are evidently some
> principles in his nature, which interest him in the fortune of others, and
> render their happiness necessary to him, though he derives nothing from it
> except the pleasure of seeing it.
> — Adam Smith
> *The Theory of Moral Sentiments, p. 9*

Adam Smith is commonly associated with the pursuit of self-interest. As the oft-quoted section above indicates, however, Smith was aware and interested in behaviors that contradict any notion of narrow self-interest. Two centuries after Smith, economics still largely assumes that individual wealth is the only, or at least the dominant, drive in human behavior. One might be tempted to think this debate concerns some subtle details on the periphery of economic theory. Quite to the contrary, some of the most fundamental results of economics rest upon specific forms of interpersonal components of preferences.

For example, narrow self-interest is an assumption in common proofs of the First Fundamental Welfare Theorem. This cornerstone of welfare economics states that, under certain conditions, free exchange will lead to Pareto optimal outcomes. The logic of the theorem is clear. If there are actions that help some people, and those individuals know

117

about the opportunities, they will act. In equilibrium, there are no uncompleted actions that would make some people happier without making others worse off. This is the definition of Pareto optimality.

So selfish acts add up to optimal social outcomes. Without the assumption of narrow self-interest, however, outcomes are not necessarily Pareto optimal. Consider, for example, a person who cares about his or her relative wealth. To be even more concrete, assume a "status-seeking" person who would prefer to be relatively wealthy. Now consider a material increasing exchange between two other people. The status-seeking person is hurt when the two other parties freely transact — their increase in wealth creates a negative externality. What appears to be a Pareto improving transaction turns out to hurt the status-seeking third party. This example extends to many forms of preferences that are richer than narrow self-interest. In these cases, the First Fundamental Welfare Theorem does not hold true, and individuals must be constrained to yield optimal societal outcomes.

The situation is very similar for the demonstration that free trade is mutually advantageous. The standard proof assumes narrow self-interest, and in its absence more restrictive assumptions about property rights are required. In macroeconomics, the assumption of narrow self-interest is often expanded to include children. This slightly modified version of self-interest is used in a variety of important macroeconomic models including the neo-classical model of growth and Robert Barro's (1974) proof of Ricardian equivalence.

Early experimental data on altruism

Guth, Schmittberger, and Schwarze (1982; GSS hereafter) had an important impact on the discussion of altruism with their laboratory studies of the ultimatum game.

The simplest ultimatum game is structured as follows. One person, called the proposer, divides an amount of money into two parts. This division is presented to a second person, termed the responder, as a take it or leave it offer (hence the name ultimatum). The responder can accept the proposed division or reject the ultimatum. In both cases the game ends with the responder's decision. If the responder rejects, then both parties receive nothing.

If both players are interested only in their own material gain, economic theory makes a clear prediction for the ultimatum game (Stahl, 1972). Consider the responder first. He must decide between some amount for himself and zero. If he cares only about his own consumption, and prefers more money to less, then any positive amount is strictly preferred to zero. The prediction is that proposers will accept any split that gives them a positive amount of money.

Now consider the proposer. Any split that gives the responder a positive amount of money will be accepted. A proposer that i) only cares about his own consumption, ii) prefers more money to less, and iii) predicts that the responder will accept all splits, will propose a split that gives the responder the smallest positive amount. Under these conditions, economic theory predicts extremely unequal proposals and no rejections.

GSS paid students to play the ultimatum game for stakes ranging from 4 to 10 German Marks. The average amount demanded by proposers was 64.9% in one group and 69% in the second group. More than 10% of offers were rejected. The results were initially disputed, but in the intervening years literally dozens of experiments have

119

confirmed the two main points: Rejection rates are significantly different than zero and offers are significantly greater than zero. Roth (ch. 4 in Kagel and Roth, 1995) provides a relatively recent summary of this literature, and points out that the experimental results agree with field data in a variety of settings ranging from labor strikes to malpractice suits.

Although the ultimatum game is one of the simplest bargaining situations, there are a variety of explanations for why behavior deviates from that predicted by narrow self-interest.

Are subjects making mistakes?

One explanation is that the subjects do not understand the situation and are making mistakes. There are two responses to this explanation. The first is that experimental attempts to remove mistakes by pre-screening and detailed explanations have not altered subjects' behavior (Kahneman et al., 1986). The second is that economics assumes agents solve a host very complex problems. For example, the neo-classical growth model and the proof of Ricardian equivalence both assume people solve intertemporal allocation problems over infinite lifetimes. If the explanation for behavior in the ultimatum game is complexity, then the validity of many economic results should be viewed with suspicion.

Are experimental data relevant?

A second explanation is that the stakes in laboratory games are too small. Hoffman, McCabe, and Smith (1995) invested $5,000 to have 50 pairs play the ultimatum game for $100. They conclude that across ultimatum experiments that vary stakes, there is a substantial decline in rejection frequency as the amount increases from $0 to $5 to $10

120

but not to $100. In other words, there is no significant difference between behavior in the $10 and $100 ultimatum game.

More evidence on the stakes in ultimatum games comes from field data. Roth catalogs a variety of real world situations that have costly and common bargaining disagreements. Finally, both battlefield and civilian heroic behavior reveals a concern for others that does not disappear as the stakes increase to the maximum possible.

Moving beyond self-interest – Formal models of altruism.

Economic theory has no difficulty constructing preferences with an interpersonal component. Gary Bolton (1991) posits a utility function that includes a term for relative consumption. In the context of two person bargaining, Bolton's model suggests that people care about the amount of money they receive <u>and</u> the percentage of the total that they receive. The ultimatum game data are consistent with a utility function of this form. Specifically, for some proposals, responders' dislike for low relative payout outweighs the value of the offer. Proposers look forward to the possible rejection and temper their behavior accordingly.

In light of Bolton's model, consider two games. The first is the standard ultimatum game as described above. The second is identical except the proposed split is generated by a computer. In the situation with computer generates splits, the responder is presented with a take it or leave it offer exactly as in the ultimatum game. The material repercussions for both individuals are identical regardless of the origin of the ultimatum.

What is the prediction for the new game? Bolton's 1991 model predicts that players will react identically in both situations. Sally Blount (1995) performed this

121

experiment and found that in the computer generated game rejection rates approach zero. The narrow self-interest model actually works better in this setting than Bolton's 1991 model.

As with the construction of Bolton's 1991 model, economic theory has no difficulty incorporating Blount's results. Several different models have been proposed that are consistent with all the data presented above. Two are presented below that take quite different approaches.

Intentions matter, Rabin 1993

Matthew Rabin (1993) modifies the utility function to include a term for intentions. If a player believes their counterpart is being **fair** (this is defined precisely by Rabin), then the player's happiness increases as the counterpart's payoff increases. Utility = U(own material payoff) **plus** some function of (counterpart's payoff). Conversely, if a player believes their counterpart is being **unfair**, then the player's happiness decreases as the counterpart's payoff increases. Utility = U(own payoff) **minus** some function of (counterpart's payoff).

Rabin's model is consistent with all the data presented above. Rejections in the standard ultimatum come from the responder perceiving the proposer as acting unfairly. In the Blount, computer-generated game, there is no unfairness on the part of the proposer hence no reason to reject.

Different utility functions for different people, Levine 1995

The narrow self-interest model, Bolton's 1991 model, and Rabin's model share a common feature that every person has a utility function of the same form. There are no spiteful or altruistic people in these models. Rather circumstances, and perceptions of circumstances, make people act in ways that can be viewed as selfish, spiteful, or altruistic.

David Levine (1995) takes an approach that can be considered orthogonal. He assumes that there are different types of people in the world. Some derive satisfaction from other's pain and some from other's pleasure. Furthermore, Levine assumes that a player's behavior is conditioned on the expectation of his counterpart's type. A person that delights in other's consumption might dislike rewarding particularly selfish types. Although the utility function differs by individual, Levine's model constraints the distribution of types to be constant across all situations.

Levine's model is consistent with the data presented so far. In the model, two groups of responders reject unequal ultimatum splits. The first group contains individuals that derive satisfaction from other's pain. They reject because the loss to them through their own payoff is more than compensated by the pleasure in hurting the proposers. The second group of rejecters is using the offer as a signal of proposer's type. Proposers who make unequal splits reveal themselves to be people who ought to be punished. In Blount's computer generated offer game, this second group does not exist, hence the lower rejection rates.

Some data on dictator games

The dictator game has the same structure as the ultimatum game except the second player does not have a right to refuse the division. Player 1's decision is unilaterally imposed (thus the name dictator). Because of this change, Player 2 is called the recipient in dictator games, as opposed to the responder in ultimatum games. Forsythe, Horowitz,

123

Savin, and Sefton (1994; hereafter FHSS) ran experiments on $5 and $10 dictator games. They report 64% of $5 dictators and 79% of $10 dictators give at least $1.

Hoffman, McCabe, and Smith (1996; hereafter HMS) run variants of the dictator game to further analyze the determinants of giving. In particular, they systematically vary what is termed the "social isolation" of the dictators. In the most socially isolated version, double blind 1 (DB1), subjects are given the amount to be divided and make a private decision. In DB1, neither the experimenter nor the recipient can identify the behavior of any individual dictator. HMS's least socially isolated treatment is a replication of FHSS (FHSS-R) where the dictator reports his or her choice to the experimenter before being paid.

HMS produce five treatments by systematically changing the conditions between FHSS-R and DB1. They report that social distance has a powerful effect on behavior. Specifically, under the DB1 treatment with $10 to distribute, 64% of offers were $0 and only 8% offered $4 or more. In contrast, under FHSS-R, 18% offers were $0 and 32% offered $4 or more. (See Figure 2 of this chapter.)

In a related study, (Grossman and Eckel, 1994), analyze dictator games where the proceeds are given to the American Red Cross. They report that this treatment doubles the average contributions as compared to a control with recipients drawn from the same subject pool as dictators.

These data are not predicted by the Levine or Rabin model. First, all dictator games produce non-zero levels of giving. Second, dictator behavior changes significantly due to factors that are not included in the Levine and Rabin models.

A genetic evolutionary prospective

Motivation

One of the fundamental facts, derived from the experimental data, is that behavior is altered by factors outside of standard game theoretic analysis. The list of additional factors includes relative payoffs, intention, and privacy. As shown above, attempts to formally incorporate all the relevant factors have failed to accurately predict behavior in dictator games; one of the simplest games imaginable.

The failure of existing modeling efforts raises the question of how to proceed. One approach is to push forward with the current program. As new factors are shown to influence behavior, they can be added to models in a formal fashion. Further experiments can be designed and the new models tested and refined.

One difficulty with the current empirical-theoretical approach, however, is that there is no way to derive the additional factors that influence behavior. Folk psychology and introspection may provide the seeds for future work, but this approach is unstructured and atheoretic.

This chapter and the experiments contained are motivated by the belief that genetic evolutionary theory can help. Darwinian theory provides a theoretical framework for the derivation of factors that are axiomatic to social sciences.

Darwinian theory has been applied to the issue of non-kin altruism. The prevailing view in biology is that all behavior, including that which appears altruistic, is motivated by genetic self-interest. The apparent paradox between motives and appearances disappears when viewed through the appropriate lens. This resolution was first and best described by

Robert Trivers (1971) as "Reciprocal Altruism". The essence of the idea is that individuals give in order to be paid back with interest.

The following sections outline a simple evolutionary model that captures the essence of Trivers' argument in an economic framework. The model is a completely standard economic model with one exception. Since the model attempts to derive a utility function, players cannot maximize utility. This assumption is replaced by the standard biological assumption, that naturally selected organisms act "as if" they seek to maximize reproductive success. The rest of the model is a straightforward two player, two period, exchange economy.

Model assumptions

Two periods = 0, 1

Two players = 1, 2

w - endowment, $w_{i,t}$ player i's endowment in period t

x - consumption, $x_{i,t}$ player i's consumption in period t

$R(\ )$ - Reproductive success, $R'(\ ) > 0$, $R'(0) = \infty$, $R'' < 0$

Assume each player tries to maximize sum of reproductive success:

Player 1:   Maximize $R(x_{1,0}) + R(x_{1,1})$

Player 2:   Maximize $R(x_{2,0}) + R(x_{2,1})$

I. Base case:

No trade, no credit market, no storage.

Player 1:   Maximize $R(x_{1,0}) + R(x_{1,1})$

s.t. $x_{1,0} \leq w_{1,0}$

$x_{1,1} \leq w_{1,1}$

➔ $x_{1,0}{}^* = w_{1,0}$ $x_{1,1}{}^* = w_{1,1}$

Similarly for player 2

In the base case, both players consume all of their endowment in each period.

127

II. Credit market

Assume each player can borrow and loan in credit market at an interest rate of r.

Player 1:

Maximize $R(x_{1,0}) + R(x_{1,1})$

subject to: $x_{1,0} + x_{1,1}/(1+r) \le w_{1,0} + w_{1,1}/(1+r)$

This is a traditional 2 good optimization with relative price = $1/(1+r)$ and

total wealth = $w_{1,0} + w_{1,1}/(1+r)$

FOC: $R'(x_{1,0}^*)/R'(x_{1,1}^*) = 1+r$

Similar FOC for player 2:

$R'(x_{2,0}^*)/R'(x_{2,1}^*) = 1+r$

Players will generally want to smooth consumption between periods. The reproductive success function is assumed to have diminishing returns, so there is a desire to move consumption from periods with high endowment to periods with low endowment.

Consider, for example, an individual who has zero endowment in period 0 and some positive endowment in period 1. The marginal value of consumption in period 0 is higher than in period 1, so the player gains by shifting consumption to period 0.

To give a concrete example, consider an individual with zero endowment in period 0 and ten units in period 1. Under reasonable assumptions about the interest rate, r, and the reproductive success function, R, the consumption bundle (4,5), for example, would be preferred to (0, 10). The player is willing to give up 5 units of consumption in period 1 in return for 4 units in period 0.

IIIa. Trade with credit markets

We now ask if players who have optimized in the credit market, can improve their outcomes by trading with each other.. Specifically, we allow players to sign a binding contract of form L_0, L_1 where:

player 1 gives player 2 L_0 in period 0

player 1 gives player 2 L_1 in period 1

Does the ability to sign such contracts improve the players' outcome? Recall Player 1's FOC from model II:

$R'(x_{1,0}^*)/R'(x_{1,1}^*) = 1+r$, or, equivalently,

$R'(x_{1,0}^*) = (1+r) R'(x_{1,1}^*)$

Recall player 1 is giving L_0 to player 2 in period 0, and giving L_1 to player 2 in period 1. Player 1 therefore always prefers smaller L_0 and L_1, whereas the preferences of Player 2 are reversed. In the presence of a credit market, with positive interest rate, equilibrium consumption in period 0 has higher marginal value. The break even point for Player 1 is $L_0 = -L_1(1+r)$ and Player 1's outcome is strictly improved if $L_0 < -L_1(1+r)$.

Now consider Player 2. The FOC is $R'(x_{2,0}^*) = (1+r) R'(x_{2,1}^*)$. This means that the break even point for Player 2 is **also** $L_0 = -L_1(1+r)$, **but** Player 2's outcome is strictly improved if $L_0 > -L_1(1+r)$.

129

The conclusion is that trade can **not** improve upon the outcome achieved by using the credit market alone. Each player uses the credit market to smooth consumption between periods and there are no remaining gains from trade.

IIIb. Trade with commitment but without credit markets:

In this section, the ability to use the credit market is removed. Players are allowed to sign binding contracts of exactly the same form as in IIIa; specifically L_0, L_1 such that

> player 1 gives player 2 L_0 in period 0.
>
> player 1 gives player 2 L_1 in period 1
>
> $x_{1,0} = w_{1,0} - L_0$, $x_{1,1} = w_{1,1} - L_1$
>
> $x_{2,0} = w_{2,0} + L_0$, $x_{2,1} = w_{2,1} + L_1$

Define: $\underline{R}_1 = R(w_{1,0}) + R(w_{1,1})$ - Reproductive success without trade or credit for player 1. Similarly for player 2,

$\underline{R}_2 = R(w_{2,0}) + R(w_{2,1})$

Define: *Zone of Potential Agreement(ZOPA)* as those contracts that make both players weakly better than the no trade condition. $(L_0, L_1) \in$ ZOPA iff L_0, L_1 satisfy:

$R(w_{1,0} - L_0) + R(w_{1,1} - L_1) \geq R(w_{1,0}) + R(w_{1,1}) = \underline{R}_1$, AND

$R(w_{2,0} + L_0) + R(w_{2,1} + L_1) \geq R(w_{2,0}) + R(w_{2,1}) = \underline{R}_2$

130

Two possible types of agreement in ZOPA

$R'(w_{1,0})/R'(w_{1,1}) < R'(w_{2,0})/R'(w_{2,1})$ $L_0 > 0, L_1 < 0$ -

   player 1 relatively satiated in period 0

$R'(w_{1,0})/R'(w_{1,1}) > R'(w_{2,0})/R'(w_{2,1})$ $L_0 < 0, L_1 > 0$ -

   player 2 relatively satiated in period 0

Define: An *Efficient outcome* is one that is not pareto dominated by another feasible

outcome.

For R's with suitable properties, a necessary and sufficient condition for an efficient

outcome is: $R'(x_{1,0})/R'(x_{1,1}) = R'(x_{2,0})/R'(x_{2,1})$

Assume that bargaining is costless. The bargaining outcome can be any L_0, L_1 in the

ZOPA that is efficient.

   The conclusion is that players will trade to improve their outcomes. In almost all

cases, one of the players will be relatively well-endowed in Period 0. Players shift

consumption away from relative wealth towards relative poverty and both can be made

better off.

IIIc. Trade without commitment:

Assume exact settings as IIIb, but players cannot commit to delivering L_1. In other words, there is no credit market, contracts between players are allowed, but not enforceable.

$\Rightarrow$ Actual amount transferred in period 1 will always be zero, $L_1 = 0$

$\Rightarrow$ Looking forward to period 1, no transfers will take place in period 0, $L_0 = 0$

If trade is possible, but there is no way to sign binding contracts, the outcome reverts to case I (classic holdup problem). In this case, because there is no credit market, mutually advantageous trades are available. The ability to achieve those trades is, however, thwarted by the non-simultaneous nature of the transaction. A player has to give up something of value in the Period 0. That player will be unwilling to make the transfer unless there is an expectation of repayment.

Interpretation of the model

Players wish to smooth their consumption because of the decreasing returns. In the presence of a credit market, players smooth consumption by borrowing and lending in the credit market. Once players have optimized through the credit market, there are no remaining gains from trade.

Without a credit market, both players can be made better off by trading in almost all situations. Specifically, as long as the relative value of endowment consumption in the two periods differs for the two players, there are gains from trade. With complete and costless contracting (IIIb), the players move to an efficient allocation that equalizes

132

marginal intertemporal trade-offs. Mutually advantageous agreements always take the form of a transfer in the first period and a reciprocal transfer in the second period.

If the players cannot commit, they face a classic hold-up problem. In the second period, the player who would give under a pareto improving contract, will always find it in his interest to deliver nothing. Looking forward to the second period, no player will be willing to make a transfer in the first period. Thus, the outcome with trade, but no commitment, is the same as the no trade outcome.

The insight of Robert Trivers

What does all of this have to do with modern human behavior? Robert Trivers (1971) contends that a significant portion of human emotional structure is designed specifically to solve the hold-up problem in a world without credit markets. His abstract is worth quoting at length:

> Regarding human reciprocal altruism, it is shown that the details of the psychological system that regulates this altruism can be explained by the model. Specifically, friendship, dislike, moralistic aggression, gratitude, sympathy, trust, suspicion, trustworthiness, aspects of guilt, and some forms of dishonesty and hypocrisy can be explained as important adaptations to regulate the altruistic system.

Trivers' argument is as follows. Ancestral humans faced a problem of smoothing consumption. Hunting produces food in large batches (a minimum of one entire animal) such that the marginal value of food to the successful hunter is small and the marginal value to the failed hunter is high. Furthermore, in the ancestral environment individual intertemporal smoothing was difficult. No formal credit markets existed and storage was difficult in a world with predators and without refrigeration.

133

In economics parlance, Trivers is interpreted as saying that preferences have a genetic component that arose by natural selection to solve the commitment problem. Specifically, people will "want" to give in situations that, in evolutionary settings, led to repayment. Similarly, people will want to reciprocate favors in settings that led to reproductive success.

Implications of model

The results of this model can be summarized in a series of statements about giving. Reciprocal altruism theory yields the following predictions:

1. Gifts flow from those with low need to those with high need. A necessary condition for reciprocal altruism is a difference in the ratios of marginal reproductive value.

2. There must be some expectation of role reversal. Condition 1, a difference in ratios of marginal reproductive value, is necessary but not sufficient. The ideal recipient has high current need and low future need.

3. *Ceteris paribus,* gifts rise as repayment probability increases. In equilibrium, if the probability of repayment is zero, there will be no gifts.

4. Gifts are altered by history. Two particular types are noteworthy. Gifts increase when there is a previous debt between the players. Gifts decrease if there has been a failure to repay in the past.

Because the mechanisms for reciprocal altruism are assumed to be genetic, the triggers for altruism reflect ancestral environments. If this theory is correct, it should be possible to engineer more or less altruism through the use of various cues. For example,

134

ceteris paribus, a cue relating to high need will promote more giving than one relating to low need. Similarly, a variety of cues about the likelihood of repayment should have predictable effects.

Reciprocal altruism and existing economic models

Reciprocal altruism theory is consistent with models such as Rabin's and Levine's. The preferences in their models can be viewed as manifestations of an underlying evolutionary process. From this perspective, the motivation for studying reciprocal altruism is to further close the gap between theory and behavior.

Robert Frank has written extensively and eloquently on altruism (see, in particular, Frank, 1986). Frank agrees with Trivers in identifying the commitment problem as the fundamental cause of altruism.[6] Frank's formal modeling, however, does not provide a model with predictive power for situations such as the dictator and ultimatum games.

---

[6] The author and Robert Frank disagree as to the completeness and adequacy of Trivers' reciprocal altruism theory (pers. comm., 1996).

135

Experimental design

Design motivation

The big picture goal of this work is to use genetic evolution theory to construct a cohesive theory of giving. Specifically, reciprocal altruism theory makes predictions that are new and testable.

The goal is to pick the experiments that are most able to distinguish among competing hypotheses. Consider by analogy, the testing of Einstein's theory of relativity. A crucial test of the theory was the prediction that gravity alters the path of light. The practical ramifications of the theory are not based on bending light by gravity, but the data confirmed Einstein's view. Similarly, the specifics of this experiment are important for their discriminatory power, not because they explain a significant amount of altruism.

On a more detailed level, this experiment is motivated by two related lines of research. The first is the empirical-theoretic work on preferences described above. The best models constructed to date predict that behavior will not be significantly influenced by variables outside the formal game structure. The most interesting laboratory exception to this prediction is the work already cited on various treatments of the dictator game. This experiment explores the ability to manipulate behavior without changing the formal structure. In particular, it provides further investigation into the double blind treatment, and it attempts to construct frames, outside the existing economic models, that will alter behavior.

The particular method of constructing the frames is motivated by the reciprocal altruism model presented in the previous section. Specifically, this experiment is an attempt to engineer higher levels of altruism through cues to the likelihood of repayment. In one treatment, recipients learn the identity of their dictator. This raises the possibility of reciprocity outside the laboratory in either a positive or negative manner. Dictators and recipients exist within the same community and there is the possibility of future interactions. Dictators who are generous may be rewarded, and dictators who are not generous may be punished.

A variety of economic models would predict increased giving when recipients know the dictator's identity. If the dictators are going to face recipients in a larger game, giving may be consistent with narrow self-interest.

This same logic does not apply to the second treatment of this experiment. In this treatment, dictators see a facial picture of their recipients, but not vice versa. With this structure there is no possible retaliation on the part of recipients. Additionally, because all the treatments are under double blind conditions, the dictators need not fear retaliation from the experimenter.

The treatment where dictators see photographs of recipients is motivated by the genetic perspective of reciprocal altruism theory. In particular, that preferences reflect ancestral and not necessarily modern problems. The recipients' picture is designed to trigger behavior through an outdated environmental cue. Until the advent of cameras, the ability to see a person, particularly their eyes, meant that they could see you. Even though dictators with recipient's pictures will "know" that their actions are private, they may not "feel" as though the acts are private, or at least not as private as without the picture.

The second research line that motivates these experiments documents the differences between face-to-face and anonymous bargaining. This literature (see Roth's ch. 4 in Kagel and Roth, 1995) reveals that subjects are much more likely to reach cooperative outcomes in face-to-face bargaining. They are also much more likely to reach symmetric agreements. One of the most salient examples of these features is a two-person bargaining game where the players have asymmetric outside opportunities (Hoffman and Spitzer, 1982.) The subjects bargain over a $14 pie where failure to agree results in $12 to a player, and $0 to the other. In face-to-face play, Hoffman and Spitzer report 100% of subject pairs agreed to $7-$7 splits.

The difference between anonymous and face-to-face bargaining would seem to be an important area of research. A large portion of laboratory bargaining is done anonymously, but most actual bargaining is done face-to-face. A difficulty in examining this question, is that experimenters lose control when bargaining is done face-to-face. The exchange of photographs in this experiment is a discrete step between anonymous and face-to-face conditions.

Three double blind treatments with precisely controlled communication

Three treatments were run in this experiment. All are variants of Hoffman, McCabe, Shachat, and Smith's (1994; hereafter HMSS) dictator design labeled Double Blind 1 (DB1).

DB1 was invented in HMSS to give maximal anonymity to the dictator. Each dictator is privately given the money to be distributed, keeps a portion, and puts the recipient's money in a sealed, opaque envelope. Decisions are made in private, and a subject, selected to monitor the experiment, handles all materials. Finally, in a twist reminiscent of a firing squad where some members have blanks rounds, two dictators are

138

given envelopes that do not contain any money. Thus, the subjects do not know the identity of their counterpart, the experimenter does not know the pairings, and the experimenter never learns the individual decisions of the dictators.

This experiment selectively removes the anonymity of the dictator pairs. The first treatment in this experiment is termed "Recipient Photo". Conditions are identical to HMSS's DB1 except that the dictator receives a photograph of the recipient before making his or her decision. The anonymity of the dictator is preserved. The experimenter never learns the actions of an individual dictator and the recipients do not discover the identity of their dictator.

The dictators answer four questions about their counterpart to ensure that they examine the photograph. The questions are designed to be neutral with respect to engendering empathy. For example, one of the questions asks if the person looks friendly (see appendix for exact text.) Questions thought to evoke sympathy such as, "How will the recipient feel after receiving your gift?" were specifically avoided.

The second treatment in this experiment is the control treatment and is termed "No Photo". Dictators in this treatment do not receive a photograph, but are asked to: "Take a moment and imagine the person you have been paired with." The No Photo dictators are then asked the exact same (verbatim) set of questions as in the Recipient Photo treatment. The No Photo treatment is identical to HMSS's DB1 with the sole exception of the questions about the imagined recipient.

The third treatment in this experiment is termed "Dictator Photo". This treatment is identical to the No Photo treatment except that the dictator's photo sent to the recipient along with the return envelope. Although the recipient learns the identity of his or her

139

dictator, the anonymity of the dictator is shielded from the experimenter and the monitor by the use of sealed envelopes. When the dictator makes his or her decision, the monitor seals the dictator's photograph into a separate envelope which is then taped to the outside of the envelope containing the dictator's distribution.

When distributing the envelopes to recipients, the monitor opens the envelope with the distribution to record its contents, but delivers the dictator's photograph to each recipient in the sealed envelope. Recipients examine their dictator's photograph in private and return the picture in a new sealed, opaque envelope. After the experiment ends, photographs are destroyed in the returned envelopes by the monitor.

Subjects

A total of 178 subjects were recruited from the undergraduate population at the University of Arizona. The dictators in this experiment had not been in any previous ESL experiments. Individuals who had been in any experiment (economic, psychology, etc.) before were asked not to enroll. The ESL's computer records were checked to verify subjects' statements (there was no way to check about experiments in other locations.) The dictators were recruited from undergraduate classes in finance, accounting or economics. Some additional subjects were recruited at the time of the experiment from the hallways of the business building.

The Economic Science Lab has a large pool of subjects who have previously participated in laboratory exercises. These individuals were used as the recipients in the experiments. Some subjects were recipients in more than one experiment. Subjects' gender and race were not recorded. Subjects appeared to be representative of the University of Arizona undergraduate population. Roughly half the subjects were women.

Dictators and Recipients for an experiment were never drawn from the same classroom. Because the experiment involves the selective removal of anonymity, it was desirable to avoid having groups of friends playing opposing roles within the same run. With the current design it is possible that subjects who received photographs recognized the person pictured. There is no evidence to suggest this occurred more frequently than a random draw from the subject pool.

Each subject was paid a $5 show-up fee. They earned more money according to the rules of the experiment. During recruitment, the subjects were told that they would earn $5 for showing up on time. They were told they could earn more money, but were specifically told that the amount could not be discussed other than to say that most previous subjects had requested to participate in more experiments.

Details of experimental conditions

All photographs were taken by the author using a Polaroid instant camera and color film. Pictures were head shots, taken at fairly close range (2-3 feet). Subjects were asked to remove any glasses and look directly at the camera. The photographs were taken as the subjects arrived, and therefore before they had any idea of the nature of the experiment.

The dictator groups were all run in the same room with the same experimenter (the author.) The subjects read the instructions to themselves and then the experimenter reread the instructions. The recipient groups were run in several different rooms.

141

Experiments were held in the late morning or early afternoon. The No photo and Dictator Photo had the same temporal pattern. Dictators came to the ESL laboratory and proceeded to make their decisions. Recipients arrived at another room after the dictators began, but before all the proposer decisions were made. Once the dictators were finished, the experimenter and the monitor distributed the outcomes to the recipients. In the No Photo and Dictator Photo treatments, the last proposer was finished in approximately one hour, and the recipients' total time was about forty five minutes.

The Recipient Photo experiment had a different temporal structure. Recipients had to arrive first so their pictures could be included with the dictators' packages. The recipients' room was on the second floor of the building. In this treatment, as in all others, the dictators made their decision in the ESL laboratory on the first floor. The recipients were free to leave between the time their picture was taken until a time estimated to be near the end of the dictators' decision period.

Results

Because of the particulars of this double blind design, a total 12 dictators were given no money to distribute. Data were collected on 74 pairs where the dictator had $10 to distribute. All of the results presented below remove twelve of $0 decisions to account for those dictators without money. The outcome of the experiment is summarized in Table 1, Figures 1 and 2.

	N	$0	$1	$2	$3	$4	$5+	avg.
No Photo	26	14	3	4	1	3	1	$1.19
Recipient Photo	24	14	0	1	2	1	6	$1.96
Dictator Photo	24	13	3	0	0	2	6	$1.71

Table 1: Distribution by dictators with $10 to distribute across all three treatments.

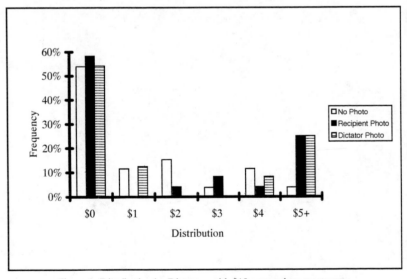

Figure 1: Distribution by Dictators with $10 across three treatments.

143

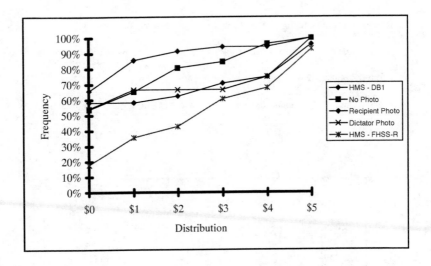

Figure 2: Cumulative Distributions for Dictators including two HMS treatments.

The double blind treatment has a strong effect on behavior. In the No Photo, Recipient Photo, and Dictator Photo treatments, 54%, 58% and 54% of dictators respectively keep all the money. Summing across all three treatments, the figure is 41 out of 74 (55%). This is consistent with HMSS figure of 64%. Furthermore, the No Photo results are not significantly different from either of HMS's double blind treatments.

Using the Wilcoxon method on the non-zero distributions yields a 82.8% and 81.2% probability that the Recipient Photo and Dictator Photo treatments are different from the No Photo treatment. Because this is below the traditional threshold for statistical significance, the following analysis of behavior should be considered preliminary.

A succinct summary of the data is, the photographs do not change the likelihood of keeping the entire $10. For dictators who do give something, however, the size of the gift is increased by the photograph treatments. Among the dictators who give, the mode for both the Recipient Photo and Dictator Photo treatments is $5 while the mode for the No Photo treatment is $2. Similarly the average for dictators who give is $3.73 under Dictator Photo, $3.92 under Recipient Photo, and $2.58 under No Photo treatments, as shown in Figure 3.

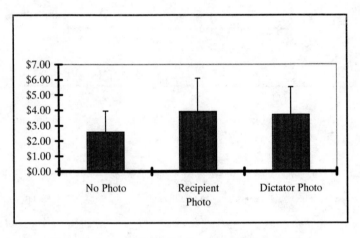

Figure 3: Average gift size for dictators who give something.

Concluding comments

The results of this experiment, when combined with the early dictator experiments, argue that behavior is significantly altered by factors outside of traditional game theory. The results are consistent with the model developed in this chapter, and are not consistent with the best existing models for interpersonal components of preferences (Rabin and Levine). This suggests that economic theory should revisit the issue of altruism and that genetic evolutionary theory may be a productive approach.

Literature cited

Andreoni, J. 1995. "Warm Glow vs. Cold Prickle: The Effect of Positive and Negative Framing on Cooperation in Experiments." *Quarterly Journal of Economics* 110(1): 1-21.

Barro, R. 1974. "Are Government Bonds Net Wealth?" *Journal of Political Economy* 81: 1095-1117.

Blount, S. 1995. "When Social Outcomes aren't Fair: The Effect of Causal Attributions on Preferences." *Organizational Behavior & Human Decision Processes* 63(2): 131-144.

Bolton, G. E. 1991. "A Comparative Model of Bargaining: Theory and Evidence." *American Economic Review* 81(5): 1096-136.

Forsythe, R., J. L. Horowitz, N. E. Savin and M. Sefton. 1994. "Fairness in Simple Bargaining Experiments." *Games and Economic Behavior* 6(3): 347-69.

Grossman, P. and C. Eckel. 1994. "Anonymity and Altruism in Dictator Games." Choice/ESA Meetings, Austin, Texas.

Guth, W. 1995. "On Ultimatum Bargaining Games -- A Personal Review." *Journal of Economic Behavior and Organization* 27(3): 329-44.

Guth, W., R. Schmittberger and B. Schwarze. 1982. "An Experimental Analysis of
Ultimatum Bargaining." *Journal of Economic Behavior and Organization* 3: 367-
388.

Hoffman, E., K. McCabe, K. Shachat and V. Smith. 1994. "Preferences, Property Rights,
and Anonymity in Bargaining Games." *Games and Economic Behavior* 7: 346-
380.

Hoffman, E., K. McCabe and V. Smith, L. 1995. "On Expectations and the Monetary
Stakes in Ultimatum Games." *International Journal of Game Theory*.

Hoffman, E., K. McCabe and V. L. Smith. 1996. "Social Distance and Other-Regarding
Behavior in Dictator Games." *American Economic Review* 86(3): 653.

Kagel, J. H. and A. E. Roth, Editors. 1995. *The Handbook of Experimental Economics.*
Princeton, N.J.: Princeton University Press.

Kahneman, D., J. L. Knetsch and R. Thaler. 1986. "Fairness and the Assumptions of
Economics." *Journal of Business* 59: S285-S300.

Kahneman, D. and A. Tversky. 1984. "Choices, Values, and Frames." *American
Psychologist* 39: 341-50.

Levine, D. 1995. "Modeling Altruism and Spitefulness in Experiments." *Unpublished
Manuscript.*

Rabin, M. 1993. "Incorporating Fairness into Game Theory and Econometrics." *American Economic Review* 83(5): 1281-1303.

Stahl, I. 1972. *Bargaining Theory.*

Tooby, J. and L. Cosmides. 1990. "The Past Explains the Present: Emotional Adaptations and the Structure of Ancestral Environments." *Ethology & Sociobiology* 11: 375-424.

Trivers, R. L. 1971. "The Evolution of Reciprocal Altruism." *Quarterly Review of Biology* 46(4): 35-57.

Appendix - Instructions to subjects

The exact text for the three treatments follows. In the Recipient Photo and Dictator

Photo sections, text that has been added to the No Photo text is *clearly marked*.

No Photo

You have been asked to participate in an economics experiment. For your participation today we have paid you $5 in cash. You may earn an additional amount of money, which will also be paid to you in cash at the end of the experiment.

In this experiment each of you will be paired with a different person who is in another room. You will not be told who these people are either during or after the experiment. This is room A.

You will notice that there are other people in the same room with you who are also participating in the experiment. You will not be paired with any of these people.

One of the persons in room A will be chosen to be the monitor for today's experiment. The monitor will be paid $10 in addition to the $5 already paid. The Monitor will be in charge of the envelopes as explained below. In addition the monitor will verify that the instructions have been followed as they appear here.

The experiment is conducted as follows: Fourteen unmarked envelopes have been placed in a box. Twelve of these envelopes contain 10 one dollar bills and 10 blank slips of paper. The remaining 2 envelopes contain 20 blank slips of paper. The monitor will be given a list of names of people in their room. He or she will call one person at a time to the back of the room, and hand each person an envelope from the box. The person who was called will then go to one of the seats, with a large box on top, in the back of the room. The envelope will then be opened privately inside the box. Only the person who was given the envelope will know what the envelope contains.

When you open your envelope you will see a page with some text and a set of questions. Answer the questions and place the page in the return envelope.

Each person in room A must then decide how many dollar bills (if any) and how many slips of paper (if any) to put in the return envelope. The number of dollar bills plus the number of slips of paper must add up to 10. The person then pockets the remaining dollar bills and slips of paper. Examples: (1) Put $2 and 8 slips in the envelope, pocket $8 and 2 slips. (2) Put $9 and 1 slip in the envelope, pocket $1 and 9 slips. These are examples only, the actual decision is up to each person. If the envelope has 20 blank slips, put 10 blank slips in the envelope and pocket the other 10. This is done in private and we ask that you tell no one of your decision. Notice that each envelope returned will look exactly the same. Also note that no one else, including the experimenter will know the personal decision of people in room A.

Once you have made your decision you will seal your envelope and place it in the box marked return envelopes. You may then leave the room.

After all fourteen envelopes have been returned, the monitor will take the box to room B. There are 14 people in room B. Each of these persons will be paid $5 to participate. The monitor will be given a list of names of people in room B. The monitor will then call up the people in room B. The monitor will choose an envelope from the box, open the envelope, record its contents, and give the contents of the envelope to the person called up. They are then free to leave. The monitor will continue until all the envelopes have been handed out and everyone else has left the room. The experiment is then over.

Recipient Photo

You have been asked to participate in an economics experiment. For your participation today we have paid you $5 in cash. You may earn an additional amount of money, which will also be paid to you in cash at the end of the experiment.

In this experiment each of you will be paired with a different person who is in another room. This is room A.

You will notice that there are other people in the same room with you who are also participating in the experiment. You will not be paired with any of these people.

One of the persons in room A will be chosen to be the monitor for today's experiment. The monitor will be paid $10 in addition to the $5 already paid. The Monitor will be in charge of the envelopes as explained below. In addition the monitor will verify that the instructions have been followed as they appear here.

The experiment is conducted as follows: Fourteen unmarked envelopes have been placed in a box. Twelve of these envelopes contain 10 one dollar bills and 10 blank slips of paper. The remaining 2 envelopes contain 20 blank slips of paper. The monitor will be given a list of names of people in their room. He or she will call one person at a time to the back of the room, and hand each person an envelope from the box. The person who was called will then go to one of the seats, with a large box on top, in the back of the room. The envelope will then be opened privately inside the box. Only the person who was given the envelope will know what the envelope contains.

When you open your envelope you will see a photograph attached to a set of questions. The photograph is of the person you have been paired with in the other room. Note, that although you will see this photograph, neither the experimenter nor the person you are paired with will learn your identity either during or after the experiment.

Answer the questions on the paper attached to the photograph and place the page and photograph into the return envelope.

Each person in room A must then decide how many dollar bills (if any) and how many slips of paper (if any) to put in the return envelope. The number of dollar bills plus the number of slips of paper must add up to 10. The person then pockets the remaining dollar bills and slips of paper. Examples: (1) Put $2 and 8 slips in the envelope, pocket $8 and 2 slips. (2) Put $9 and 1 slip in the envelope, pocket $1 and 9 slips. These are examples only, the actual decision is up to each person. If the envelope has 20 blank slips, put 10 blank slips in the envelope and pocket the other 10. This is done in private and we ask that you tell no one of your decision. Notice that each envelope returned will look exactly the same. Also note that no one else, including the experimenter will know the personal decision of people in room A.

Once you have made your decision you will seal your envelope and place it in the box marked return envelopes. You may then leave the room.

After all fourteen envelopes have been returned, the monitor will take the box to room B. There are 14 people in room B. Each of these persons will be paid $5 to participate. *The monitor will choose an envelope from the box, open the envelope, record its contents, remove the photograph and questions page, and give the contents of the envelope to the person in the photograph.* They are then free to leave. The monitor will continue until all the envelopes have been handed out and everyone else has left the room. The experiment is then over.

150

Dictator Photo

You have been asked to participate in an economics experiment. For your participation today we have paid you $5 in cash. You may earn an additional amount of money, which will also be paid to you in cash at the end of the experiment.

In this experiment each of you will be paired with a different person who is in another room. You will not be told who these people are either during or after the experiment. This is room A.

The person you have been paired with will receive a photograph of you. No one else will see the photograph of you, and the photograph will be destroyed after the experiment.

You will notice that there are other people in the same room with you who are also participating in the experiment. You will not be paired with any of these people.

One of the persons in room A will be chosen to be the monitor for today's experiment. The monitor will be paid $10 in addition to the $5 already paid. The Monitor will be in charge of the envelopes as explained below. In addition the monitor will verify that the instructions have been followed as they appear here.

The experiment is conducted as follows: Fourteen unmarked envelopes have been placed in a box. Twelve of these envelopes contain 10 one dollar bills and 10 blank slips of paper. The remaining 2 envelopes contain 20 blank slips of paper. The monitor will be given a list of names of people in their room. He or she will call one person at a time to the back of the room, and hand each person an envelope from the box. The person who was called will then go to one of the seats, with a large box on top, in the back of the room. The envelope will then be opened privately inside the box. Only the person who was given the envelope will know what the envelope contains.

When you open your envelope you will see a page with some text and a set of questions. Answer the questions and place the page in the return envelope.

Each person in room A must then decide how many dollar bills (if any) and how many slips of paper (if any) to put in the return envelope. The number of dollar bills plus the number of slips of paper must add up to 10. The person then pockets the remaining dollar bills and slips of paper. Examples: (1) Put $2 and 8 slips in the envelope, pocket $8 and 2 slips. (2) Put $9 and 1 slip in the envelope, pocket $1 and 9 slips. These are examples only, the actual decision is up to each person. If the envelope has 20 blank slips, put 10 blank slips in the envelope and pocket the other 10. This is done in private and we ask that you tell no one of your decision. Notice that each envelope returned will look exactly the same. Also note that no one else, including the experimenter will know the personal decision of people in room A.

Once you have made your decision you will seal your envelope and bring it to the monitor. The monitor will seal your photograph in a separate envelope and tape it to your return envelope. Your return envelope will then be placed it in the box marked return envelopes. You may then leave the room.

After all fourteen envelopes have been returned, the monitor will take the box to room B. There are 14 people in room B. Each of these persons will be paid $5 to participate. The monitor will be given a list of names of people in room B. The monitor will then call up the people in room B. ***The monitor will choose an envelope from the box, open the return envelope, record its contents, and give the contents of the return envelope and the sealed envelope with the photograph to the person called up.***

The person will examine the photograph in private and return the photograph sealed in a new envelope. They are then free to leave. The monitor will continue until all the envelopes have been handed out and everyone else has left the room. The experiment is then over. The photographs will not be removed from the second sealed envelope and will be destroyed.

151